HEALTH HAZARDS MANUAL FOR ARTISTS

Michael McCann, PhD.

■

Published by the
FOUNDATION FOR THE COMMUNITY OF ARTISTS
New York, New York

Published by the
Foundation for the Community of Artists
280 Broadway/Suite 412 • New York, NY 10007
212/227-3770

ISBN:0-933-032-00-5
Library of Congress Catalog #78-70898

PRINTED IN USA

Table of Contents

About the Author

Michael McCann, PhD., is an industrial hygienist and science writer specializing in the occupational health hazards of arts and crafts materials. He is a frequent writer, lecturer and consultant on art hazards and is president of the Center for Occupational Hazards, which operates the Art Hazards Information Center. His forthcoming book, *Art Hazards and Precautions: A Handbook for Artists and Craftspeople*, is due to be published by Watson-Guptill in 1979.

Preface to Revised Edition

In the three years since the publication of the *Health Hazards Manual for Artists*, the issue of the occupational health problems of arts and crafts materials has become of great concern to many artists, craftspeople and art teachers. The realization that many of the art materials in common use are hazardous and are causing illness has alarmed many artists and led to demands for adequate information on these hazards and how to eliminate them. This demand has shown itself in large audiences at many lectures and workshops on art hazards, the hundreds of enquiries received at the Art Information Center (5 Beekman Street, New York, NY 10038, 212/227-6220 and in the fact that the *Health Hazards Manual for Artists* has sold over 10,000 copies.

This revised edition of the pamphlet has several purposes. It updates and in some cases reorganizes the old material, and it includes new material. This new material mostly comes from articles in my Art Hazards News column which appeared in *Art Workers News*, and includes new sections on commerical art materials, children's art materials, stained glass, dyeing and reproductive hazards from art materials. The section on children's art materials was written with Monona Rossol, M.S., M.F.A. who has taught children and been concerned for many years about the hazards of children's art materials. Ms. Rossol is also associated with the Art Hazards Information Center. I hope that these revisions and additions will make this pamphlet even more useful to artists and craftspeople.

Michael McCann, Ph.D.
July, 1978

Preface to First Edition

Artists and craftspeople, like other workers, have a right to work in a safe environment. It is apparent, however, that many of the materials used by artists and craftspeople are hazardous and present a threat to their health. The N.Y. Chapter of the National Art Workers Community therefore resolves that:

1. Art schools have a responsibility to set an example of how to work safely with art materials. Art schools should provide safe working conditions and should include as an integral part of their curriculum information on the health hazards of art materials and how to work with them safely.

2. Artists and craftspeople have a right to know the hazards of the materials with which they are working. Therefore, art suppliers should fully label their art materials both as to composition and hazards. In addition, art suppliers should undertake research to develop the safest art materials possible.

3. Art supply stores should support full-disclosure labelling of art materials and should pressure art suppliers to conform with this standard.

4. Municipal, state and federal governments should pass adequate legislation for full-disclosure labelling of art materials and any other legislation needed to protect the right to work in a safe environment.

5. Government agencies should sponsor research to investigate the occupational health problems of artists and craftspeople and should provide free medical treatment where necessary.

The preceding resolution, passed by NAWC and endorsed by the Foundation for the Community of Artists, resulted from the concern generated by the series of articles, "Health Hazards in Art," which I wrote for *Art Workers News*. These articles created a flood of letters from artists describing their own experiences and asking for more information. It soon became clear that there were two basic problems: the question of adequate labelling of art materials as to their hazards, and the question of the dissemination of information about the hazards of art materials and how to work with them safely.

The question of labelling is crucial because if you don't know what is in a particular material, there is no way to know the potential hazard of working with it. I believe that full-disclosure labelling is necessary. This means that all the contents of art materials should be listed on the label, along with their hazards and necessary precautions. In order to achieve this, art organizations and artists will have to put pressure on art suppliers, and on those government agencies like the Consumer Products Safety Commission whose responsibility it is to make certain that materials are properly labelled.

The other main problem is that of education. Information on the health hazards of art materials and how to work with them safely should be widely disseminated throughout the art education system. Art students at every level should receive this information at the same time they learn the various art techniques so that it becomes part of their work habits. In order to make the information in the *Art Workers News* articles available to a larger audience, the Foundation for the Community of Artists decided to reprint the entire series in the present booklet form. I have updated the information where needed and added an index to make the booklet more useful as a reference.

How can the information in this booklet best be used? The purpose of the articles and the present booklet is to give the working artist or craftsperson a good idea of the hazards of the materials he or she is using, and suggestions on how to work with them safely. In many cases it is not known whether a particular material will cause health problems to an artist using it. Since very little research has been done on the medical problems of artists and their materials, I have had to go by whether the material has created problems amongst industrial workers. In some cases, industrial workers have a greater exposure to these materials than artists and would, therefore, be expected to have greater problems. However, in many cases, I have found that artists are working with toxic materials under much more hazardous conditions that are commonly found in industry, usually because of the complete lack of safety precautions on the part of the artists. Therefore, I believe that industrial experience is a good guideline to determine whether a material might be hazardous for artists, at least until medical studies prove otherwise.

A major factor in determining the degree of hazard in using toxic materials is the susceptibility of the artist using the material. A person's susceptibility to a particular material depends upon a variety of factors, including age, state of health, the environment and the target organ of the material. These various factors can be used to define *high risk groups.*

Children are a particular high risk group because of their size (amount of toxic materials which would not affect an adult can harm a child), and because of the immaturity of their body tissues. Small children and infants are particularly susceptible to lung problems because of their small air passageways and lungs. Therefore extreme care should be taken to not expose children to toxic art materials, whether in a home studio or in art classes for children.

Other high risk groups include people with allergies, smokers, excessive drinkers, older people and people with disease-weakened or damaged organs (particularly the heart, lungs and liver). In addition, environmental factors such as excessive air pollution and exposure to other chemicals can significantly affect a person's susceptibility to health problems created by exposure to art materials.

Finally, I want to discuss how to tell if you are poisoning yourself with your art materials. If you find that you are experiencing new or unusual symptoms during or after work, then you might be working unsafely with your materials. These symptoms can include headaches, dizziness, fatigue, blurred vision, nausea, nervousness, chronic coughing, loss of appetite, skin problems, irritability, breathing difficulties, etc. If these symptoms persist, you should see a doctor. When doing so, take along a list of all the materials with which you are working so that the doctor can determine whether the materials might be the cause of your symptoms. If you are working with highly toxic materials like lead, barium, toxic solvents, silica dust, etc., then you should have regular check-ups to make sure that they are not affecting your health. In any case, remember that art materials, like many other chemicals, may be hazardous to your health and should be handled accordingly.

Michael McCann, Ph.D.
July, 1975

How Art Materials Affect You

Are the materials you are working with slowly killing you? Or maybe they are just going to make you chronically ill. Scary? I hope so, because many of the materials artists are working with are much more dangerous than is commonly believed. Many people look at the warning labels on materials and figure that companies are playing it safe. This is not true. In fact, most of the warnings are vague and understated.

For example, one common paint and varnish solvent containing benzol (benzene, not to be confused with benzine (V.M.&P. Naptha) carries the following warning:

DANGER! POISON!

MAY BE FATAL OR CAUSE BLINDNESS IF SWALLOWED. FLAMMABLE. VAPOR HARMFUL. SKIN AND EYE IRRITANT. CONTAINS BENZOL, ACETONE AND METHANOL. CANNOT BE MADE NONPOISONOUS.

If swallowed, do not induce vomiting. CALL PHYSICIAN IMMEDIATELY. Remove patient to fresh air, but have him lie down and keep warm. Cover eyes to exclude light. In case of contact with eyes, flood repeatedly with water. Keep away from heat, sparks and open flame. Close container after each use. Avoid prolonged or repeated breathing of vapor and contact with skin or eyes. Use only with adequate ventilaton.

KEEP OUT OF THE REACH OF CHILDREN.

What the label does not tell you is that benzol "can penetrate the skin..., has a definite cumulative action...and...daily exposure to concentrations of 100 ppm (parts per million) or less will usually cause damage if continued over a protracted period of time." (*Dangerous Properties of Industrial Materials* by N. Irving Sax, Reinhold Publishing Corporation, New York, 1957). It destroys the bone marrow which forms red and white blood cells and is even known to cause leukemia in some people. For this reason, the Consumer Product Safety Commission in 1978 proposed a ban on paint strippers and other consumer products containing benzene (benzol).

The major danger of benzol is not an immediate one, but a long-term effect. This is what doctors call a chronic effect; that is, one which appears gradually over a long period and is often due to repeated exposures to small amounts of material. Chronic diseases are much harder to diagnose because the symptoms are often vague and don't appear at the time of exposure. For example, the early symptoms of chronic benzol poisoning can include fatigue, headache, dizziness, nausea and loss of appetite, loss of weight and weakness. These types of symptoms can often be mistaken for other mild ailments like the flu until it is too late. Such chronic reaction to art materials is often the real problem, not the immediate acute type of poisoning which is much more readily diagnosed. In fact, many toxicologists believe that such chronic poisoning is much more common among artists than is generally believed.

This is not unique with artists. Similar results are being found in industry. And doctors are finding that many so-called safe substances aren't really safe at all. Occupational health and safety, as a result is a growing concern of many unions which view it as a more important issue than wages.

The range of dangerous materials is very broad. It includes traditional art materials like lead paints and pottery glazes, solvents, inks, welding fumes, wood and plastic dusts from sanding, and a wide variety of new plastics materials.

Factors affecting risk

Just how hazardous to health are these art materials? The actual risk involved depends on several factors, most importantly length, frequency and amount of exposure, the toxicity of the material, total body burden, effects of exposure to several chemicals and personal susceptibility.

For example, an artist who is exposed only to a cup of a toxic solvent for a few minutes a day is much less likely to develop problems than an artist who might use several pints of the same solvent over a period of some hours. Similarly, exposure to toxic materials once a week or month is much less hazardous than daily exposure.

The toxicity of an art material determines how much exposure to the material it can take to cause body damage. For example, small amounts of lead pigment can cause poisoning if ingested, whereas the body can tolerate much larger amounts of iron oxide pigments without ill effects. Of course, you must remember that you might be exposed to a particular toxic chemical from several sources. The total resulting exposure is called the total body burden for that chemical. The total body burden of lead could not only come from accidentally ingested lead pigment, but could also include exposure from automobile fumes, water pollution, cigarette smoking, nearby lead smelters, lead solders, lead glazes and enamels, etc.

Exposure to many different chemicals can also increase the risk and extent of injury to a particular organ. For example, damage to the lungs resulting from excess exposure to etching gases can be intensified by simultaneous exposure to carbon arc gases, solvent vapors, cigarette smoke, air pollution, etc. In some cases this effect is not a simple additive effect but can be a multiplicative or synergistic effect. An example is smoking and asbestos exposure. Smokers have about a tenfold increased risk of lung cancer compared to nonsmokers. Nonsmokers who work with asbestos also appear to have an excess risk of lung cancer. Smokers who work with asbestos, however, have a 92 times increased risk of lung cancer. Similarly exposure to many chlorinated solvents (e.g. carbon tetrachloride or trichloroethylene) and alcoholic beverages can have a serious synergistic effect.

Finally, personal susceptibility can affect the actual degree of hazards. As discussed in the preface, children, people with allergies, chronic heart, liver or lung problems, heavy drinkers, smokers and the elderly are all high risk groups.

Entry Into The Body

There are three ways in which toxic substances can enter the body: 1) by skin contact, 2) through breathing, and 3) through the mouth and the digestive system.

Skin contact is the most frequent method.

Our skin has a defensive barrier consisting of an outer waxy coating and a layer of dead cells intertwined with a tough protein called keratin. Normally this barrier protects the skin against chemicals and physical injury. However, many substances—acids, caustic alkalis, organic solvents, peroxides, bleaches, etc.—can destroy this protective coating and attack the skin layers underneath, causing various types of skin ailments.

Some chemicals—phenol (carbolic acid), benzol, toluene and methyl alcohol, for example, can even penetrate further and enter the bloodstream to travel to other parts of the body. By stripping away the protective waxy skin coating, many organic solvents make it possible for other chemicals to penetrate the skin's barrier. Obviously, the way to prevent these hazardous substances from entering the body through the skin is to ensure that the chemical never comes in contact with the skin.

The second method for substances to enter the body is through breathing in their vapours or dusts. This is the most common way in which substances harming internal organs enter the body. Some of these—for example, glacial acetic acid (a "stop bath" in photography), welding fumes, noxious gases resulting from overheating of many plastics—can immediately damage the sensitive linings of the airways and lungs. Others, especially dusts, can cause chronic diseases. One of the important factors here is the size of the particles. Finer particles are more toxic. Large particles can get trapped by the mucus of the nose and upper breathing passages, where they can be swallowed or spit out.

Whether or not a substance gets beyond the lungs to affect the rest of the body depends on whether it is soluble in the blood.

The third method of exposure is through the mouth and digestive system. This occurs more often than many people realize through mouth contact with contaminated hands, food and cigarettes. This can be a problem for artists whose studios are in their living quarters. The materials travel from the mouth to the digestive system. Another source of ingestion is inhaled dusts which are swallowed. Once in the stomach, the body's defenses act to absorb the harm-

2

ful materials into the bloodstream slowly, and in small amounts. However, this is often not sufficient to prevent damage, especially with chronic, cumulative poisons.

Now that we have seen the various ways in which dangerous substances can get into the body, let's look at some of the specific ways in which these substances can harm us.

The Skin

As mentioned earlier, many materials can harm the skin directly. In fact, skin ailments are the most frequent kind of occupational hazard caused by chemical substances. Most artists that I have talked to have had at some time or another a rash, burn or other skin problem caused by working with art materials.

Skin diseases caused by chemicals are mostly of two types: direct irritation and allergies.

Chemicals that cause direct irritation or dermatitis are called primary irritants, and affect everyone who comes in contact with them. The types of damage that can appear are reddening, itching, blistering, thickening, hardening and flaking. In some cases, it takes a long time and repeated exposures to show damage. The condition lasts as long as exposure continues and usually disappears after contact is ended. Primary irritants commonly encountered by artists include acids, alkalis, organic solvents (benzol, toluol and other aromatic solvents and chlorinated hydrocarbons, turpentine, petroleum solvents, ketone, etc.) plastics materials (including many resins, monomers, catalysts, fillers, etc.) and such others as aniline, arsenic compounds and fiber glass.

Besides primary irritants which affect everybody, many substances are sensitizers and cause allergies. Sensitizers affect only some people, although some are so strong they will affect most people. Allergies don't occur at the first exposure. Often a person can work with a material for years before developing a sensitivity to it. After that, however, the sensitivity never disappears and even very small amounts of the material can bring on the allergic reaction.

Sensitizers work by reacting with skin proteins and changing them so that the body produces antibodies to the changed protein as if it were a foreign protein. These antibodies cause inflammation of the skin upon subsequent exposure to the chemical. A common example is allergy to poison ivy. Some common sensitizers that affect many people include many plastics materials (in particular epoxy resins and amine hardeners), bichromate salts, nickel salts, formaldehyde, and turpentine.

Skin cancer is another type of skin disease that is of concern. The major problem is that we don't know whether many common chemicals cause cancer or not because cancers usually take 20-30 years to develop. Some substances—including arsenic compounds, coal tar dyes, paraffins, lamp black—have been definitely shown to cause cancer.

Lungs

Acute lung diseases result when strongly irritating substances (such as ammonia, nitric acid etching gases, glacial acetic acid, ozone from welding) burn the tissues of the air sacs in the lung. This results in the air sacs filling with fluid, a condition called pulmonary edema, making it difficult to breathe. Pneumonia is often a complication of this disease.

Chronic lung diseases, such as chronic bronchitis and emphysema, can result from repeated exposures over several years to irritating substances. This results in damage to the larger airways in the lungs which lead to the air sacs. Over the years, these chronic diseases worsen and result in more and more coughing and mucus production and an increased susceptibility to respiratory infections. Smoking is the major cause of these diseases.

Another major form of lung disease is pulmonary fibrosis, a permanent scarring of the lung tissue. This can result from continual exposure to dusts, such as that produced from sanding some woods or silica dust from clay and some stones. This is similar to miners' black lung.

Many materials including Western Red Cedar sawdust, formaldehyde, cold water dyes, isocyanates (found in polyurethane resins), epoxy hardeners, and turpentine can cause asthma or other respiratory allergies.

3

Blood

Chemical substances that affect the red and white blood cells in blood can have very serious effects. The red blood cells are essential to the transport of oxygen to body tissues and white blood cells make antibodies and help fight infection. The actual oxygen-carrying molecule in red blood cells is hemoglobin. Chemicals like carbon monoxide, aniline, some dyes and photographic developers can affect the hemoglobin so that it can no longer carry oxygen, leading to oxygen starvation and possibly death. Aniline, toluol, benzol, lead and other substances can damage the red blood cell membrane and cause the cell to rupture. This can result in symptoms like weakness, fatigue, palpitations, a pale complexion and anemia. I mentioned the bone-marrow-destroying properties of benzene earlier. This results in a lack of red and white blood cells and platelets, and can be fatal. Benzene (benzol) may also cause leukemia.

Liver

One of the liver's main functions is to detoxify substances, both those that enter the body from outside and those that the body produces. However, it has a limited capacity to do this and liver damage can result when this capacity is exceeded. Further, when the liver is damaged it can't detoxify the body's own toxins, leading to more damage.

One common symptom of liver damage is jaundice, a yellowish or greenish coloring of the skin. Other symptoms of liver damage tend to be vague and can include tenderness or swelling of the liver, nausea and loss of appetite. One type of liver disease is hepatitis or inflammation of the liver. Hepatitis is known as a viral disease, but it can also be caused by chemical substances. Hepatitis will usually heal without lasting damage except in severe cases. Then scarring of the liver (cirrhosis of the liver) can result. Some typical substances that can cause liver damage are the chlorinated hydrocarbons, metals like antimony and cadmium, benzol, dioxane, alcohols, styrene, phenol, and cellosolve (ethylene glycol monoethyl ether).

Nervous System

The nervous system is very susceptible to damage, and except for some of the peripheral nerves, damage is permanent. In particular, the brain can only survive for a few minutes without oxygen and so chemicals that interfere with oxygen supply cause brain damage. The brain can also be poisoned by chemical substances like carbon disulfide and hydrogen cyanide (which can be produced in thermal decomposition of polyurethanes). Heavy metals, like lead, mercury, and arsenic can cause nerve-function disorders and even death.

Many substances have an anesthetic action and cause depression of the central nervous system. This is particularly dangerous, since you might not notice the effects: slow reflexes and drowsiness, leading possibly to accidents. Organic solvents like alcohols, chlorinated hydrocarbons, ethers, toluene, xylene and ketones are especially noted for this.

Some chemicals can damage the peripheral nervous system (hands, arms, feet and legs). Examples include lead, mercury, methyl butyl ketone and hexane (found in low-boiling naphtha and rubber, cement thinners).

The Reproductive System

Do men and women react differently to toxic chemicals? This was the topic of a Washington Conference on Women and the Workplace. The general feeling was that, aside from chemicals affecting the reproductive system and pregnancy, there is not much difference. The main reasons for these exceptions are the difference in sex organs and the fact that only women can get pregnant.

We can divide the effects of chemicals on reproduction into three basic categories: effects prior to pregnancy, effects during pregnancy, and effects on the new-born infant and child.

Prior to pregnancy, chemicals (including those used in art) may affect both men and women. Reactions include interference with sexual function (e.g., loss of sex drive), lowered fertility, genetic damage and difficulty in conceiving. Women can develop menstrual disorders, and men can develop problems with the testes and prostate.

Lead, for example, causes menstrual dis-

4

orders in women, and loss of sex drive, atrophy of testes and possible sperm alteration in men. It is also thought to cause decreased fertility and mutations. Carbon disulfide, a solvent, also severely affects the reproductive systems of both men and women. Cadmium and manganese may affect the male reproductive system.

Chemicals causing genetic damage are of particular concern because even low exposures may cause mutations. Exposure to mutagens (mutation-causing chemicals) commonly result in spontaneous abortions, and birth defects which can be passed on from generation to generation. Exposure of either men or women may result in mutations since either the man's sperm or the woman's egg can be damaged. For example, a recent study showed that wives of vinyl chloride workers had more stillbirths and miscarriages than other women. Other chemicals that are mutagenic or are suspected of being mutagenic include benzene, lead, trichloroethylene, and anesthetic gases. Many other chemicals have been shown to be mutagenic in animal studies, but they have not been studied in people.

Chemicals causing damage during pregnancy can affect either the pregnant woman or the developing fetus. In the first case, the effect is due to the fact that during pregnancy a woman's metabolism is very different from normal. Anemia is a common problem and chemicals like lead and benzol which can cause anemia are particularly hazardous. In addition, pregnant women are susceptible to respiratory problems and certain types of physical strain.

Many chemicals—called teratogens—can damage the growing fetus, even when present in very small amounts, and cause severe birth defects and frequent miscarriages. Thalidomide is a classic example. Chemicals which have been shown to cross the placenta and which may damage the fetus include many metals (lead, cadmium, etc.); many organic solvents (benzol, chlorinated hydrocarbons, carbon disulfide); carbon monoxide (cigarette smoking causes underweight babies); anesthetic gases, aspirin and many others. In addition, some chemicals may cause cancer in the children of women exposed to them during pregnancy. Examples are some pesticides and diethylstilbestrol (DES).

Finally, many chemicals can injure infants and children. One example is poisoning of an infant caused by breastfeeding when the mother has been exposed to toxic chemicals. (For example, methylene chloride has been shown to be present in the mother's milk up to 17 hours after exposure). Other problems include exposure caused by children being present when toxic substances are being used, and the carrying home of toxic dusts on clothes and shoes. For example, some children of lead workers have developed lead poisoning from lead carried home on the father's clothes.

Recommendations: One major problem is that most chemicals—including most art materials—have not been tested to see if they cause mutations before pregnancy or damage the fetus during pregnancy. It is clear that many chemicals do so, and can have these effects in small amounts. Pregnant women should not work with art materials which could enter the bloodstream—and from there the fetus—unless it can be shown that they are not being exposed. This includes exposure from skin contact, inhalation or accidental ingestion. (In cases of pregnant women exposed to these materials at work, this brings up questions of paid furloughs or job transfers without loss of pay or seniority, as is the practice in several European countries.)

The basic problem with this approach is that often a woman does not know she is pregnant for several weeks, and it is the first 12 weeks of pregnancy that are the most hazardous. This makes it crucial for a woman to find out if she is pregnant as soon as possible.

Chemicals causing mutations (e.g., lead, vinyl chloride) also fall into the category where neither men nor women should risk exposure, since artists cannot work safely with these materials.

Overall, the solution to these problems is to identify which chemicals are dangerous and to get rid of them, and to minimize exposure to all chemicals so that you are protected from as yet unidentified chemicals which might cause mutations or affect the growth of the fetus.

Other Organs

Many of the materials artists and craftspeople use may also affect other body organs. For example, kidney damage can result from exposure to lead, arsenic, cadmium, chlorinated hydrocarbons, etc. Bladder cancer may result from exposure to benzidine-derived direct dyes (used for dyeing cotton and silk). Barium, methylene chloride and smoking may damage the heart. These are only a few examples of the types of injury that chemicals used in art materials may cause.

Solvents, Aerosol Sprays, Acids and Alkalis

Solvents

In general, solvents are one of the most underrated hazards in art. They are used for a million purposes: to dissolve and mix with oils, resins, varnishes, inks; to remove paint, varnish, lacquers; to clean brushes, tools, silk screens, and even hands. As a result, artists are continually being exposed to solvents.

Almost all organic solvents are poisonous if swallowed or inhaled in sufficient quantity, and most cause dermatitis after sufficient skin contact. High concentrations of most solvents can cause narcosis (dizziness, nausea, fatigue, loss of coordination, coma, etc.). This can increase the chances for mistakes and accidents. Some solvents—for example, benzol (benzene) and carbon tetrachloride—are so toxic that they shouldn't be used. Other solvents—for example, acetone and ethanol (ethyl or grain alcohol)—are reasonably safe.

Solvents fall into several classes with similar properties. If one member of a class of solvents is toxic, usually another safer member can be chosen.

Alcohols are generally anaesthetics and irritants of the eyes and upper respiratory tract. In high concentrations, methanol (wood or methyl alcohol) can cause dizziness, intoxication, blurred vision and possible liver and kidney damage. If swallowed it can cause blindness and even death. Ethanol, available as denatured alcohol containing some methanol, is a safer solvent. Amyl alcohol acts on the nervous system causing dizziness, nausea, vomiting and double vision. Uses: shellac thinner,

paint and varnish remover, lacquer thinners, etc.

Aromatic hydrocarbons are among the most dangerous solvents. In general they are narcotic and irritating to the skin. the most dangerous is benzol (benzene), which causes chronic poisoning from the cumulative effect of exposure to small amounts. Its effects are destruction of bone marrow, leading to loss of red and white blood cells, and sometimes leukemia. Toluol (toluene) doesn't have the long term chronic effects of benzene, but its immediate effects can be more severe if a person is exposed to a high enough concentration. With proper ventilation, however, toluol is a suggested replacement for benzol. Xylol (xylene) is similar to toluol and may cause some chronic blood damage. Uses: resin solvent, paint and varnish remover, fluorescent dye solvent, common silk screening wash-up, lacquer thinners, aerosol spray cans, etc.

Chlorinated hydrocarbons, like aromatic hydrocarbons, are very hazardous. Some have been used as anaesthetics in the past, but were found to be too toxic. All of them dissolve the fatty layer of the skin and can cause dermatitis. They also cause liver and kidney damage. The drinking of alcohol after exposure to chlorinated hydrocarbons can make people very sick. One of the most toxic chlorinated hydrocarbons is carbon tetrachloride and it shouldn't be used. It can be absorbed through the skin and exposure to small amounts can cause severe liver and kidney damage. Exposure to larger amounts can cause unconsciousness and death. Other toxic chlorinated hydrocarbons include tetrachloroethane (acetylene tetrachloride), chloroform, ethylene dichloride, perchloroethylene and trichloroethylene. The last four solvents have been shown to cause liver cancer in mice. Methyl chloroform (1,1,1-trichloroethane) appears to be less toxic than other chlorinated hydrocarbons, although it may cause heart problems. Methylene chloride (dichloromethane) is highly volatile and high concentrations may cause narcosis, lung irritation and pulmonary edema. Methylene chloride also decomposes in the body to form carbon monoxide and inhalation of large amounts has resulted in fatal heart attacks. People with heart problems and smokers are particularly at high risk. Although most of the chlorinated hydrocarbons are not flammable, they may decompose in the presence of ultraviolet light or excess heat (e.g., a lit cigarette) to form the poison gas phosgene. In general try to replace chlorinated hydrocarbons with less toxic solvents. Uses: wax, oil, resin, grease and plastics solvent, paint strippers.

Petroleum distillates tend to be less toxic than most other solvents. They have a mild narcotic effect and can cause lung irritation in large amounts. If ingested, they may cause pulmonary edema and possible death due to aspiration into the lungs. Petroleum distillates are also skin irritants. Hexane, one of the most volatile petroleum distillates, may cause peripheral neuritis—nerve inflammation and possible paralysis of arms and legs—from chronic inhalation of large amounts. Hexane is found in "extremely flammable" rubber cement thinners and in low-boiling naptha (petroleum ether). Other petroleum distillates in increasing order of boiling point are gasoline, benzine (VM&P Naphtha), mineral spirits (odorless paint thinner, white spirits) and kerosene. Uses: paint thinners, rubber cement thinners, silk screen poster inks, clean-up solvent, etc.

Esters are eye, nose and throat irritants and have anesthetic effects. Most common acetates are not skin irritants or sensitizers. Ethyl acetate is the least toxic, followed by methyl and amyl acetates. Methyl cellosolve acetate (ethylene glycol monomethyl ether acetate) is very toxic, causing anemia and other blood diseases. It is dangerous both through inhalation and through skin contact. Methyl cellosolve is similar to the acetate. Cellosolve (ethylene glycol monoethyl ether) and cellosolve acetate are less toxic than the methyl counterparts. Uses: lacquer, resin and plastic solvent.

Ketones cause narcosis and irritation to the eyes and upper respiratory tract in high concentrations. Their odor-warning properties are a good indication of the degree of exposure. They also cause defatting of the skin upon prolonged exposure, resulting in dry, scaly, cracked skin. Acetone is one of the safest solvents (except for its high flammability) and does not seem to have any lasting effects. Methyl ethyl ketone (MEK) is more toxic than acetone. Methyl butyl ketone may cause peripheral neuritis. In some cases this has resulted in paralysis of arms and legs. Uses: Solvent for

lacquers, oils, waxes and plastics.

Other solvents include ethyl ether, a very volatile lacquer solvent and anesthetic, and turpentine. The latter is a very common oil paint and varnish thinner. Turpentine is a skin irritant and sensitizer for many people. Its vapors are irritating to the eyes, nose and throat upon prolonged exposure. Resulting symptoms include headaches, gastritis, anxiety, and mental confusion. Turpentine is highly poisonous by ingestion, with one tablespoon being fatal to a child.

Aerosol Sprays

Artists are using a multitude of aerosol sprays today: fixatives, retouching sprays, paint sprays, varnishes, adhesive sprays, etc. Aerosol sprays are very dangerous unless used in such a way as to not breathe the vapors. The fine mists containing possible toxic substances, such as paints, varnish, adhesives, etc., can travel long distances before settling. Further, they penetrate deep into the lungs. Besides the dangers from the substances dissolved in the sprays, the solvents and propellants are often a hazard.

For example, many sprays contain toluol and chlorinated hydrocarbons. In spray form, these solvents may be more dangerous than in vapor form because the mists contain larger quantities of solvent. Concern about propellants mounted when it was disclosed that many spray products contained vinyl chloride, a chemical that has been shown to cause liver cancer. These products have been withdrawn from the market. Many propellants and solvents used in aerosol cans are highly flammable.

Air brushes and spray guns are also hazardous since they produce fine mists which can enter the lungs.

Acids and Alkalis

Acids cause burning of the skin, especially when concentrated. If acid is spilled on your skin, wash with lots of water. An important safety rule with acids is to add the acid to the water, not the other way around. Strong acids include acetic, carbolic (phenol), chromic, hydrochloric, nitric, sulfuric, hydrofluoric and perchloric acids. Chromic acid is also a skin sensitizer. The fumes from etching metals with nitric acid

7

are very dangerous since they burn the lungs and may result in pulmonary edema (fluid in the lungs). Exposure to excessive nitric acid fumes can be fatal. Uses: cleaning metals, etching metals, dyeing.

Alkalis cause burning of the skin and eyes, and ulcers. Potassium (caustic potash) and sodium hydroxide (caustic soda) are the most dangerous; other alkalis that cause burns are sodium carbonate, potassium carbonate, calcium oxide (quicklime or unslaked lime), calcium hydroxide (slaked lime), sodium metasilicate, sodium silicate and ammonia. Ammonia vapors and quicklime dust can also damage the lungs.

Painting

Painters use many different media: traditional ones like oil, tempera, encaustic, water color, gouache and fresco; and modern ones, mostly acrylic, but including media like ethyl silicate, vinyl acetate and other synthetics. In these media, the artist used many different pigments, vehicles, solvents (thinners, paint and varnish removers, etc.), varnishes and other materials.

Pigments

Most artists are aware of the dangers of lead pigments and don't handle them in powder form because of the danger of inhaling the dust. Even ready-to-use lead paints are very dangerous to handle, and such precautions as carefully washing hands and cleaning fingernails after using them is crucial, to avoid accidental carrying to the mouth and subsequent ingestion. Many artists, however, are not aware that many other pigments in common use are also very toxic due to the presence of other toxic metals. Inhalation or ingestion of these can also lead to chronic poisoning, and similar precautions should be taken with such pigments. (See Table 1.) In particular, the habit of pointing a brush with the lips can result in the ingestion of hazardous pigments. Chrome yellow (lead chromate) and zinc yellow (zinc chromate) powders may cause lung cancer if inhaled. Cadium pigments may cause kidney damage and prostate cancer.

Table I—Toxic Pigments

Arsenic:	Emerald green, cobalt violet (cobalt arsenate type)
Antimony:	true Naples Yellow (lead antimoniate)
Cadmium:	all cadmium pigments
Chromium:	chromium oxide green, zinc yellow, strontium yellow, viridian, chrome yellow
Lead:	flake white, mixed white, true Naples yellow, chrome yellow
Manganese:	manganese blue, manganese violet, burnt umber, raw umber, Mars brown
Mercury:	vermillion, cadmium vermillion red

Other pigments besides ones containing heavy metals can be hazardous. Lamp black, for example, can cause cancer upon repeated skin contact. In addition, the toxicity of many of the modern synthetic pigments is unknown. Some of the metallic driers used with pigments are also toxic because they contain lead or manganese. Cobalt linoleate is the least toxic drier.

Vehicles

The vehicles and binders used in the traditional media (drying oils, egg yolk, gums, casein, etc.) are essentially nontoxic. One exception is quicklime, which is both a skin and lung irritant, with inhalation of the dust leading to chemical pneumonia. The modern synthetic vehicles are acrylic, acrylic/vinyl and vinyl resins. The resins themselves are nontoxic and, except for the pigments, so are the ready-to-use polymer colors (water emulsions). Quickdrying acrylic colors can be made by suspending pigments in solutions of certain acrylic powders in mineral spirits, turpentine or toluol. Some hazard might be associated with the use of toluol in particular.

Some acrylic emulsions, particularly media, contain ammonia. This causes the odor of some acrylic emulsions and may cause irritation of the eyes, nose and throat if used without ventilation. Some acrylic paints contain mercury preservatives.

Chronic accidental ingestion of such paints has caused mercury poisoning.

Varnishes

Here the solvents are the major hazard. The various solvents used include methyl alcohol and ethanol (shellac varnish), turpentine (damar, mastic and cooked oil-resin varnishes), and the lacquer solvents used with pyroxylin (nitrocellulose) and other synthetic resins. The major hazard in lacquer thinners is due to the presence of toluene or xylene.

Ceramics

In ceramics, health hazards fall into two main categories: handling of the raw materials and inhalation of the fumes during firing of the pottery.

Clays

Clays contain silicates and free silica (SiO2). Inhalation of silica dust from handling the clay in dry form can lead to silicosis or "potter's rot." Symptoms may take years to develop and include shortness of breath, decreased chest expansion and increased susceptibility to infections. Eventually severe scarring of the lungs can result. Inhaling large quantities of kaolin dust, can also cause a mechanical clogging of the lungs called kaolinosis. The most hazardous operations are the mixing of clay dust, and breaking up dry grog. The contamination of the studio with dry clay dust is also a major hazard.

Glazes and Colorants

The dusts created by the grinding and handling of some of the raw materials used for colors and glazes can also create silicosis, especially high silica materials like flint, feldspar and talc. Another hazard of the colorants and glazes is that many of the minerals used contain highly toxic metals. Inhalation of the dusts (e.g., in spraying) or ingestion of these materials can lead to serious chronic poisoning.

Among glaze minerals, those containing lead are highly toxic. The use of lead frits

decreases but does not eliminate the hazard. Other toxic glaze materials include barium carbonate, asbestos and alkali oxides.

Many of the colorants contain toxic metals like antimony, chromium, manganese, uranium, cadmium and vanadium. Nickel compounds are skin sensitizers and possible cancer causing agents. Chromates (lead chromate, zinc chromate and iron chromate) may cause lung cancer.

Firing

During the firing process, toxic fumes and gases are produced. This can include fluorine, chlorine, and sulfur dioxide from the breakdown of the raw glazes to the oxides, and also the possible release of toxic metal fumes from the glazes and colorants (With fritted glazes, the gases are not produced since that happened during the fritting stage.) Many of these same gases, especially sulfur dioxide, may be released during bisque firings. In addition, gas-fired kilns are a source of carbon monoxide. Therefore it is essential that kilns be ventilated to the outside atmosphere, either by chimneys (as are used for gas-fired kilns), or through an overhead hood ventilation system.

Traditional Sculpture and Casting

Sculptors use a wide variety of materials, including stone, wood, metals, clay, plastics, etc. The hazards involved in working with these materials vary from mild to extreme, depending upon the particular substance. In this section the different sculpture materials and methods are considered.

Stone

Sculptors use a variety of techniques to work stone, including chipping, grinding and carving. Some hazards are obvious: for example, the danger of eye injury from flying chips. This is why sculptors should always wear protective goggles when chipping or grinding.

But there is also a long-term danger from working with certain stones—that of silicosis. Known to many workers as "grinder's consumption" or "stonemason's disease," silicosis results from the repeated inhalation of dust containing free silica. As previously noted, silicosis affects breathing capacity, resistance to respiratory disease, and results in scar tissue in the lungs.

Stones containing large amounts of free silica include quartz (100% silica), granite, sandstone, brownstone, slate, jaspar, opal, amethyst, onyx and sometimes soapstone. Other stones that may contain some free silica include diabase, dolomite, travertine, serpentine and some forms of marble and limestone.

Soapstone, serpentine and greenstone often contain asbestos as a contaminant. Inhalation of asbestos can cause lung cancer, mesothelioma (cancer of the lining of the chest and abdominal cavity).

If you work with pneumatic tools, other dangers are present. The vibration can cause "white fingers" or "dead fingers," a circulatory system disease also known as Raynaud's phenomenon. This particularly happens when the hands are chilled and can cause permanent disability. In addition the noise from the pneumatic equipment, unless muffled properly, can cause hearing loss.

Woods

Woodworkers are subject to a large number of occupational health problems resulting from exposure to the woods, especially tropical woods, solvents, adhesives, noise and vibration.

Many woods can cause skin irritation and allergies, including South American boxwood, cocobolo, ebony, American and African mahogany, mansonia, East Indian and Brazil rosewood, East Indian and other satinwoods and Western Red Cedar.

Chronic inhalation of sawdust can cause chronic respiratory diseases. In particular, cocobolo, ebony, African mahogany, mansonia, rosewood and satinwood can cause respiratory irritation and allergies. Beech, iroko, Western Red Cedar and teak can cause severe asthma. South American boxwood, cork oak, redwood and some maple sawdusts can cause an acute illness resembling pneumonia. It appears a few hours after exposure with symptoms of shortness of breath, dry coughing, chills, sweating, fever and weight loss. A person with this usually recovers from a first attack without any ill effects, but repeated exposures can cause lung scarring and decreased lung capacity.

Woodworkers are also at higher risk than the the rest of the population for developing nasal and nasal sinus cancer. This disease occurs in 7 in 10,000 woodworkers, usually after about 40 years of exposure.

Paint strippers contain many different toxic solvents, including toluene, methyl alcohol, methylene ch1oride and—up to 1978—benzene (benzol), which can cause leukemia. Other hazards faced by woodworkers include toxic preservatives, adhesives (e.g. epoxy resins, cyanoacrylate glues, formaldehyde resins, non water-based contact adhesives), and vibration and noise from pneumatic tools.

Modeling and Molding Materials

Modeling clays come in two basic forms, water-based and oil-based. The latter is often sold under the name plasticine.

The main hazard of clays is from the inhalation of free silica found in many clays. If the clay is kept moist and the work area kept clear of clay dust, this is not a problem.

The dust from plaster of paris (calcium sulfate) is irritating to the eyes and respiratory tract, and a dust mask should be worn when dust is created. When casting, sometimes metallic paints and marble dust are added to the surface for special effects. These additives might create hazards.

Metal Casting

Most sculptors send out large pieces to a commercial foundry to have them cast into metal by the shell molding process, but a few do their own casting. In addition, many sculptors cast small pieces of sculpture themselves by the lost-wax process. The commonest metals and alloys used are bronze, brass, pewter, copper, lead, iron, aluminium and stainless steel. Gold, silver and platinum are sometimes used for small pieces.

In the casting process, the metal is melted and then poured into a suitable negative mold. The fumes of many of these metals and alloys are toxic, especially the lead found in brass and pewter. In addition, lead is sometimes added to molten bronze. Inhalation of these lead fumes or of the lead oxide dust found in the dross can cause lead poisoning.

The metal fumes may also cause an acute disease called metal fume fever. This is especially true of zinc oxide fumes, but oxides of copper, iron, magnesium and nickel can also cause metal-fume fever. Symptoms are very similar to that of the flu—chills, fever, nausea, weakness and aches—and appear a few hours after exposure. Metal-fume fever lasts about a day and a half, but recovery is complete.

Another problem is the carbon monoxide produced from incomplete combustion of fuels, and from the burning of sea coal and other organic materials found in the molding sand. This is a problem during pourng and for some time after.

The sand used in the shell molding process has a high silica content and the dust should not be breathed. The phenol-formaldehyde or urea-formaldehyde resins used as binders can decompose from the heat of the process to produce toxic formaldehyde, phenolic and/or ammonia vapors. In addition, the hexamethylenetetramine used as a catalyst for the resin is a strong skin, ear, eye, nose and throat irritant and a skin sensitizer.

In the lost-wax process, the fire-resistant plaster or clay used as a negative mold contains many additives which are hazardous. This includes silica flour which can cause rapidly developing silicosis, solvents and acids. Good ventilation or approved respirators should be used.

A variation of the lost wax process uses polyurethane foam or styrofoam to make the positive mold. Decomposition of the foam during the molding process can release toxic gases and requires careful ventilation.

Another major hazard in casting is the large amount of heat released. Unless workers are shielded from the heat, they may develop heat stress diseases. In addition the infrared (IR) radiation produced can cause burns unless the skin is covered. Unless proper goggles are worn, exposure of eyes to IR may cause heat cataracts.

Welding, Soldering and Brazing

Welding

I shall only consider the hazards involved in oxyacetylene and electric arc welding, since these are the methods most likely to be used by sculptors.

Physical hazards in welding include the danger of fire, electric shock from arc welding equipment, burns caused by molten metal sparks and burns caused by excessive exposure to infrared, visible and ultraviolet radiation. Infrared and visible radiation generate large amounts of heat which can cause burns, headaches, fatigue and eye damage. Ultraviolet radiation can cause severe sunburn and prolonged exposure may lead to skin tumors. Electric arc-welders in particular are subject to pink eye (conjunctivitis) and some have cornea damage from exposure to the UV radiation. These hazards point out the need for careful skin and eye protection when welding.

Chemical hazards depend on the type of welding technique and on the metals being welded. Oxyacetylene torches produce carbon dioxide, which can replace the normal oxygen in the air, carbon monoxide, which ties up the blood's hemoglobin, and also unburned acetylene, which is a mild intoxicant and can cut off the oxygen supply to cause rapid breathing and air hunger. In addition, commercial acetylene contains small amounts of other toxic gases and impurities.

Metal welding, particularly arc-welding, produces enough energy to convert the air's nitrogen and oxygen to nitrogen oxides and ozone. Nitrogen oxides are highly corrosive to the eyes, nose and respiratory tract. Exposure to large amounts can cause fluid to accumulate in the lungs, emphysema and even death. Ozone is an eye, nose and throat irritant and it is a severe lung irritant, causing fluid in the lungs, hemorrhage, shortness of breath, headache and drowsiness.

If welding is carried on within 200 feet of decreasing solvents (chlorinated hydrocarbons), phosgene can be produced by the action of ultraviolet radiation on the chlorinated hydrocarbons. Even minute amounts of phosgene, a poison gas used by the Germans in World War I, can be deadly, and its effects often don't appear for hours after exposure.

Metal fumes are generated by the vaporization of metals, metal alloys, and of the electrodes used in arc-welding. In addition, fluoride fluxes produce fluoride fumes. These fumes dissolve in the lungs to produce hydrofluoric acid, which is highly corrosive and can cause severe burning of the lungs besides affecting teeth, bones, skin and other parts of the body.

Many metal dusts and fumes cause skin irritation and sensitization. This includes brass dust (copper, zinc, lead and tin), cadmium, nickel, titanium and chromium.

As mentioned under metal casting, many metal fumes, especially those of zinc and copper, can cause metal fume fever. Some metals also cause more severe problems, especially lead, cadmium, chromium and manganese. Lead poisoning is well known, chromium causes bronchial asthma and sometimes lung cancer, and manganese causes manganism, a disease resembling Parkinson's disease. Inhalation of cadmium fumes can cause a disease initially resembling metal fume fever but which can be fatal.

Welding of stainless steel is particularly hazardous because the nickel present in the alloy reacts at welding temperatures to produce nickel carbonyl. This is an extremely toxic vapor that causes headaches, dizziness, nervous system disorders, pulmonary edema and possibly allergic bronchial asthma. In addition nickel fumes or dust may cause lung cancer.

In addition there are problems in welding materials that may be coated with various substances. For example, many metals are coated with lead paint, mercury-containing anti-fouling paint, cadmium plating, etc.

Soldering and Brazing

These techniques are considered here because they do fall under the category of joining metals by heat. Only instead of melting the metals to be joined as in welding, a third metal of lower melting point is used to join them.

In soft soldering, the temperatures are below 700° and tin/lead solders are used. At these temperatures there is little hazard

from lead vapors unless a person spends long periods of time regularly soldering and has his or her face close to the point of soldering. The fluxes produce very irritating gases, especially zinc chloride and acid fluxes. For these reasons, there should be good ventilation. Brazing (hard or silver soldering) is considerably more hazardous because of the higher temperatures.

In addition some solders contain other toxic metals, such as cadmium. Cadmium fumes can cause severe lung and kidney disease and death. In fact, one person died in 1967 from inhaling cadmium fumes when brazing with a silver solder containing cadmium.

Many low melting, easy flow silver solders contain substantial amounts of cadmium. These are supposed to be labelled as containing cadmium but usually aren't. Fluoride fluxes often used with silver solder are highly toxic if inhaled.

Plastics

Plastics are used in every part of our lives without any harmful effects that we know of. But the processes used to make and fabricate plastics can be very dangerous. Many occupational diseases are found among plastics workers. And sculptors using these processes are subject to the same diseases.

The degree of hazard depends on whether you are making the plastic or are working with the finished plastic (that is, sanding, cutting, carving, vacuum-forming, etc.).

Plastics consist of large numbers of long chain-like molecules made from small molecules (called monomers) linked together. These long chain-like molecules are called polymers, and the process of linking the monomers together is called polymerization. In *thermoplastics*, the polymers lie side by side and can move when heated to fill different shapes. In *thermosetting* plastics, on the other hand, the long polymeric molecules are joined together or "cross-linked" by smaller molecules or by heat. The process of turning thermoplastics into thermosetting ones by cross-linking is called curing. Heating thermosetting plastics does not change their shape. The greatest hazards arise when you are working with the monomers, solvents, fillers, catalysts, hardeners, etc. used in making plastics. Many of the monomers in particular are toxic. This is what you are doing when you are working with casting, laminating and foam processes.

The hazards involved in working with the finished plastics come mostly from the methods used to work the plastic. Overheating or burning of plastic can result in the release of toxic gases from the decomposition of the plastic. This can occur during sawing or machining. Heating of plastics can sometimes result in the release of unreacted monomer which is trapped in the plastic. Plastic dusts created in the sawing, sanding and polishing of plastics can create lung problems. And the glues and cements used to bond plastics often contain toxic solvents and plastics monomers.

With these factors in mind, let's look at the hazards involved in working with particular plastics.

Acrylics

The main hazards in working with the finished acrylic sheets and blocks (Plexiglass and Lucite) are in inhalation of the dusts or heat decomposition products and in the use of acrylic glues and cements. Cements consist either of pure solvents (dichloromethane, ethylene dichloride, trichloroethane) or of acrylic chips dissolved in these solvents. These solvents require careful ventilation. Some acrylic glues consist of acrylic monomers and have the same hazards as are involved in polymerizing these monomers, as discussed below. They can be recognized by the fact that two or more components have to be mixed.

Methyl methacrylate (MMA) monomer or combinations of MMA with acrylic polymers can be used for casting and laminating. When combined with a catalyst (e.g., benzoyl peroxide), and heated, the mixture cures to a clear solid.

Methyl methacrylate is a strong skin sensitizer and irritant, and its vapors cause nausea, loss of appetite, headaches, and lowering of blood pressure. Benzoyl peroxide, like most peroxides, is flammable, explosive, a skin irritant, and a skin sensitizer. Peroxides are also very damaging to

the eyes and care should be taken to avoid contact with the eyes.

Polyester

Polyester resins used for casting and laminating are very hazardous and require excellent ventilation or respirators. The normal resin consists of a nontoxic polyester dissolved in styrene monomer which acts as a cross-linker. To cure the resin, a catalyst (methyl ethyl ketone peroxide or benzoyl peroxide) is added.

Styrene monomer is an aromatic hydrocarbon, and like other aromatics, it is hazardous. The National Safety Council's *Accident Prevention Manual for Industrial Operations* says that styrene monomer is "irritating to the eyes, respiratory tract, and produces an extremely severe dermatitis." Dr. Susan Daum and Dr. Jeanne Stellman, in "Work Is Dangerous To Your Health," say that styrene "can cause headache, nausea, appetite loss and even coma. Low concentrations can damage the liver, cause blood damage and affect the nervous system." When working with polyester resins, don't use styrene as a clean-up solvent. Use acetone instead.

Some polyester resins are modified by the addition of methyl methacrylate monomer or vinyl toluene. the latter is also a hazardous aromatic hydrocarbon. The hazards of the peroxide catalysts have already been discussed.

The dangers of working with polyester resins was described by the sculptor Robert Mallary in an article called "The Air of Art Is Poisoned," *Art News*, October, 1963.

Epoxy Resins

Epoxy resins are used in laminating, casting, glues and lacquer coatings. They consist of two components: an uncured epoxy resin and a hardener. The liquid, uncured epoxy resin is a skin irritant, sensitizer and suspected cancer-causing agent because of its chemical formula. The hardeners, especially amines, are very strong sensitizers and irritants in minute quantities, and have been a major source of adverse reactions among users. During the curing process, large amounts of heat are produced which can cause dangerous fuming of the hardener. Overheating of the cured resin during sawing, sanding, etc. can produce irritating decomposition products. Handling of epoxies requires careful precautions to avoid skin contact and inhalation.

Polyurethanes

Polyurethanes are used in several forms: urethane rubber is used as a flexible mold, urethane foam can be used for sculptures or cast. They consist of two components: an isocyanate one, and a polyol component which also contains catalysts and other additives.

Polyurethanes are very dangerous to make. According to the Upjohn Chemical Division, "Inhalation of isocyanate vapors ...has caused progressive disabling illness characterized by breathlessness, chest discomfort, and reduced pulmonary function. Massive exposure to high concentrations has caused, within minutes, irritation of the trachea and larynx and severe coughing spasms. Massive exposure may also lead to bronchitis, bronchial spasm and/or pulmonary edema (chemical pneumonitis)." Small amounts can cause allergic reactions in the lungs leading to "asthmatic attacks and respiratory distress." Isocyanates can also cause skin and eye problems. The catalysts used are irritating to eyes, lungs and upper respiratory tract, and may cause liver and kidney damage, skin sensitization and irritation. Fluorocarbon blowing agents used with foams may cause loss of feeling and unconsciousness at high concentrations.

Obviously, making polyurethanes is very hazardous. In casting polyurethanes, be sure to wear an approved respirator. Spray polyurethane foams are even more hazardous to work with because of the mist produced. Upjohn recommends that people doing spraying use chemical-type goggles, skin protection and air-supplied respirators or gas masks. I would recommend that only sculptors willing to take extreme precautions should use spray polyurethane foam. It is too toxic for casual use.

Vinyl Polymers

These include polyvinyl chloride (PVC), polyvinyl acetate (PVA), PVC/PVA copolymers and polyvinyl alcohol. They are ther-

moplastics and can be heat molded, vacuum formed, etc. In heat welding of PVC at high temperatures, care must be taken to avoid breathing toxic hydrogen chloride fumes released from the decomposition of PVC. There might be some hazard in heating PVC pellets or powder if the polymer contains any unreacted vinyl chloride monomer, since the monomer has been shown to cause chemical hepatitis and liver cancer at low levels. The solvents used can be toxic.

Polystyrenes

Polystyrene is available as sheets which can be cut, shaped, etc., as molding pellets which can be fused, as foam sheets (Styrofoam) which can be cut with hot wire cutters, and as expandable polystyrene beads for foam molding. Cutting or sawing of factory-fresh or very large slabs of Styrofoam releases the colorless, odorless gas methyl chloride, and can release any trapped styrene monomer. In small amounts, methyl chloride can cause symptoms of drunkenness; in large amounts, dizziness, staggering and even death. Open flames should be avoided when using expandable polystyrene beads since they contain flammable pentane gas. Some styrene cements used to cement styrofoam contain styrene monomer.

Others

Room temperature vulcanizing (RTV) silicone rubber is a common mold-making material. A two-component system, the only hazard is with the catalyst component Rubber cement, used in paste-up, is dissolved in petroleum distillates. Prolonged breathing of these vapors should be avoided. Fluorocarbons (e.g., Teflon, TPFE) are safe unless heated to decomposition. The decomposition products can cause polymer fume fever, which is similar to metal fume fever. Moderate heat, for example, cigarettes, can create this problem.

Additives

There are many different types of additives, including fillers, colorants, stabilizers, plasticizers, etc. I shall only comment on a few of the more hazardous. Fiberglass is commonly used in laminating. It is very irritating to the skin and causes many fine cuts which make it easier for other chemicals to cause irritation. Dust respirators should be worn when sanding plastics containing fiberglass, since the glass dust can cause severe lung damage and behaves like asbestos in animals. Many fillers contain free silica, and inhalation of the dust should be avoided. Probably the most hazardous substance to use is asbestos. Inhalation of even small amounts of asbestos dust can cause cancer. In general, many additives are hazardous, so skin contact and inhalation of vapors or dusts should be avoided.

Printmaking

Print-making methods use a variety of solvents and solvent mixtures, primarily in cleaning. Again, aromatic hydrocarbons (benzol, xylol, and toluol) and other lacquer solvents are hazardous and should be used with adequate ventilation. Benzol should be avoided. Cleaning should be done with as nontoxic a solvent as possible.

Inks used in black-and-white printing usually contain carbon black. Repeated contact with carbon black can cause skin cancer years later. Avoidance of skin contact and careful washing after exposure is helpful. Common toxic pigments used in printmaking include chrome yellow (lead chromate), zinc yellow (zinc chromate), Milori green (contains lead chromate), and the cadmium colors (see also Table I). The hazards of the organic pigments have not been well studied, but there is growing concern about their toxicity.

Silk Screening

In silk screening, the solvents are the biggest health hazards, with the greatest exposure coming during printing, drying of the prints and wash-up. Very careful ventilation of work areas is needed to prevent a dangerous build-up of vapors in the air. Ideally, drying of the prints should done in an enclosed drying cabinet with exhaust ventilation if at all possible. Since most of the solvents are skin irritants, skin contact with them should be avoided as much as possible through use of gloves, especially during wash-ups.

The solvents used depend on the type of ink and the stencil or media used. For example, most poster, enamel and fluorescent inks can be washed up with mineral spirits. Many companies suggest using aromatic solvents like xylol for many inks. Although these are often more efficient, they are also more toxic. Lacquer inks and plastic inks, on the other hand, require the more toxic lacquer solvents like MEK, acetates, etc.

Relief Printing

Traditional wood-cutting and engraving present few hazards. Modern relief methods may be more hazardous, especially those using solvents and glues. Linoleum etching uses caustic soda (sodium hydroxide) which can cause very severe skin burns.

Intaglio

Etching grounds basically consist of asphaltum (pitch in oil or turpentine base), beeswax and rosin; liquid grounds also contain solvents like benzine, or in the case of some commercial ones, ether or methyl chloroform. The asphalt or pitch is a skin irritant and may cause skin cancer. Rosin dust is a sensitizer, and inhalation can cause hayfever-type symptoms and possible asthma. This is particularly a problem in aquatinting. Rosin dust is explosive and there have been explosions involving rosin dust boxes resulting from sparks generated by the rubbing of metal parts.

One of the greatest hazards in intaglio is the etches, particularly the acids. Acids, especially when concentrated, cause severe skin burns. Eye damage from splashes can also be very dangerous. One rule is to *always add acid to water*, never the reverse. Nitric acid etching of copper and zinc produces highly toxic nitrogen oxide fumes which can dissolve in the lungs to cause pulmonary edema and chemical pneumonia. Hydrochloric acid (used in Dutch mordant) can cause similar severe lung problems. Potassium chlorate, also used in Dutch mordant, is a skin irritant and, when mixed with organic materials, is explosive.

Mixing of the hydrochloric acid and potassium chlorate releases poisonous chlorine gas. Potassium dichromate, used in some etches, is a strong irritant and strong sensitizer. It can cause deep ulcerous burns to skin and nasal membranes, even to the extent of perforating the nasal septum.

Lithography

One of the biggest hazards in lithography is potassium dichromate. It is used in a variety of art materials, including some desensitizing etches, and fountain solutions. Chrome alum, used in one type of desensitizing etch, is similar to dichromates in toxicity. Desensitizing etches also use nitric and phosphoric acids. The danger here is in handling of concentrated acids. Litho crayons and litho tushe contain lamp black, which may cause skin cancer. Some talcs (French chalk) or talc/rosin mixtures contain asbestos, which can cause asbestosis, lung cancer and mesothelioma (a rare cancer). An asbestos-free talc should be chosen.

Photo Techniques

Photo litho, photo etching and photo silk screening are common techniques today. The greatest hazard in these techniques lies in the widespread use of unvented carbon arcs as a lighting source. Carbon electrodes consist of carbon, tar, pitch, rare earth fillers and a copper coating. When lit, the carbon arc produces toxic carbon monoxide, nitrogen oxides, ozone and toxic metal fumes. The gases and fumes, especially ozone and nitrogen oxides, can cause chronic lung problems, including emphysema after repeated exposure. One problem is that dangerous amounts of fumes can be inhaled without noticeable discomfort. Carbon arcs must be directly vented to the outside by an overhead or canopy hood. In addition, carbon arcs produce large amounts of ultraviolet light which can cause severe eye damage if UV-absorbing goggles or hand shields are not used. Walls should be painted with UV-absorbing zinc oxide paint to reduce reflection of UV light.

Photo etching uses several toxic solvents. Kodak KPR Photo-Resist for example, contains ethylene glycol monomethylether acetate, which affects the blood, liver and nervous system both through inhalation and through skin absorption. The KPR developer and dye both contain toluol. Gloves should be worn when handling these chemicals and careful ventilation is essential.

Photo silk screen uses two types of systems: direct emulsions and indirect emulsions. Most direct emulsions use ammonium dichromate as the sensitizer. Like potassium dichromate, the ammonium salt is a strong irritant and sensitizer. Silver nitrate, used as sensitizer in Rockland Super Fast Emulsion SC-12, is also very corrosive to the skin. In addition the developer for SC-12 contains caustic soda (sodium hydroxide) which can cause severe skin burns. Indirect emulsions use presensitized films and hydrogen peroxide as developer. Concentrated hydrogen peroxide can cause eye damage and prolonged skin contact can cause blisters.

Photography

Many of the chemicals used in photographic processing can cause severe skin problems, and, in some cases, lung problems through inhalation of dusts and vapors. The greatest hazard occurs during the preparation and handling of concentrated stock solutions of the various chemicals. During these steps in particular, it is essential to wear protective gloves and goggles (to protect against splashes). Special care should be taken to avoid skin contact with powders and to avoid stirring up dusts which can be inhaled. Good ventilation is important to get rid of vapors, especially from the fixer.

Black-and-white processing includes developing, stop bath, fixing and rinsing steps. The developer usually consists of hydroquinone and Metol (monomethyl p-aminophenol sulfate), both of which can cause skin irritation and allergic reactions. Developers are highly toxic by ingestion, causing methemoglobinemia and cyanosis (blue lips and fingernails due to oxygen deficiency). These are dissolved in an alkaline solution containing sodium sulfite and sodium carbonate or sodium hydroxide. These chemicals can cause skin irritation and even burns. Hands should never be put into the developer. If skin contact does occur, the skin should be washed copiously with water and then with an acid-type skin cleanser.

The stop-bath consists of a weak solution of acetic acid. The concentrated acid can cause burns, and inhalation of the vapors can irritate the breathing passages and throat. Potassium chrome alum, sometimes used as a stop hardener, contains chromium and can cause ulcerations, especially in cuts and nasal membranes, and allergies.

The fixer usually contains sodium sulfite, acetic acid, sodium thiosulfate (hypo), boric acid and potassium alum. Hypo and the mixture of sodium sulfite and acetic acid produce sulfur dioxide which is highly corrosive to the lungs. Potassium alum, a hardener, is a weak sensitizer and may cause some skin dermatitis.

Many intensifiers (bleaches) can be very dangerous. The common two-component chrome intensifiers contain potassium dichromate and hydrochloric acid. The separate components can cause burns, and the mixture produces chromic acid. Its vapors are very corrosive and may cause lung cancer. Handling of the powder of another intensifier, mercuric chloride, is very hazardous because of possible inhalation of the dusts and resultant mercury poisoning. Mercuric chloride is also a skin irritant and can be absorbed through the skin.

The commonest reducer contains potassium ferricyanide. If it comes into contact with heat or concentrated acids, the extremely poisonous hydrogen cyanide gas may be released.

Many toners contain highly toxic chemicals. These include selenium, uranium, liver of sulfur (corrosive to skin and breathing passages), gold and platinum (allergies) and oxalic acid (corrosive).

Hardeners and stabilizers often contain formaldehyde which is very poisonous, very irritating to the eyes, throat and breathing passages, and can cause dermatitis, severe allergies and asthma. Some of the solutions used to clean negatives contain harmful chlorinated hydrocarbons.

Color processing involves many of the same chemicals as are used in black-and-white processing. Developers also contain dye couplers, which can cause severe skin problems, and some solutions contain toxic organic solvents.

Textile Arts

The textile arts include a variety of processes, including spinning, weaving, crocheting, knitting, dyeing, photoprinting, etc. I will discuss only some of the main hazards here.

Fiber Arts

Most of the hazards in the fiber arts comes from dust problems. This is particularly a hazard in early stages of processing like spinning where fiber dust is present. Most fiber dusts can cause respiratory irritation and sometimes allergies when inhaled regularly. Cotton, flax and hemp dusts can cause brown lung or byssinosis after years of exposure. In its early stages symptoms of shortness of breath, chest tightness and increased sputum flow appear only when a person returns to work after a few days' absence. This stage is reversible. In more advanced stages, symptoms are very serious and are present all the time. At this stage the disease is not reversible and resembles chronic bronchitis and emphysema.

Imported animal fibers, especially sheep's wool or yarn and hairs have the risk of anthrax a serious bacterial disease due to the presence of anthrax spores. This has two forms: a skin form and an inhalation form ("wool-sorters disease"). The inhalation form is usually fatal and in 1976 a California weaver died of this. All imported wool or yarn should be decontaminated before purchase.

Other hazards with fibers or fabric include respiratory allergies or irritation from synthetic materials due to possible presence of formaldehyde resins, physical strain from constant uncomfortable positions in weaving, and the use of toxic chemicals (e.g. fire retardants).

Dyeing

Hazards in dyeing come from both the dyes, mordants and other dyeing assistants. Direct dyes used for cotton, linen and

17

rayon often are made from benzidine-type derivatives. These dyes may cause bladder cancer. Silk kimono painters in Japan who use these dyes, for example, have a high rate of bladder cancer. This may in part be due to their habit of pointing their brush with their lips. All-purpose household dyes contain a mixture of direct, acid and basic dyes and therefore have the same hazards.

Fiber-reactive or cold water dyes can cause severe respiratory allergies, usually after several years of exposure. Pre-reduced or pre-solubilized vat dyes are caustic to the skin and respiratory system. Lye (sodium hydroxide), caustic soda and sodium hydrosulfite used as dyeing assistants with vat dyes are also very corrosive.

Azoic or naphthol dyes come in two parts, a "fast salt" and a "fast Base." They may cause dermatitis and hyperpigmentation. Their long term effects have not been studied. The long term effects of acid dyes used for silk and wool, have also not been studied. Acetic acid, formic acid and sulfuric acid, sometimes used as dyeing assistants with acid dyes, can cause eye and respiratory irritation and skin burns. Glauber's salt (sodium sulfate) used with acid dyes is not very toxic. Basic dyes, used for wool silk and some synthetics, may cause allergic responses in some people.

The long term hazards of natural and synthetic mordant dyes have not been studied. However many of the mordants used with these dyes can be hazardous. In particular sodium or ammonium dichromate can cause allergies, burns and skin ulcers. Inhalation may also cause perforation of the nasal septum. Other mordants are also toxic, especially copper sulfate, ammonia and oxalic acid.

Wax used in batik is a fire hazard when molten. If overheated, the wax decomposes to release highly irritating acrolein fumes. This is particularly a problem when ironing out the wax. This process should be well ventilated. If using solvents, do not use the extremely toxic carbon tetrachloride. Instead use benzine (V.M. & P. Naphtha) or send your piece to the cleaners.

Photoprinting

The ferric ammonium citrate and potassium ferricyanide used in blueprint-ing (cyanotype) are only slightly toxic. The silver nitrate used in brownprinting (Van Dyke process) is moderately corrosive by skin contact and inhalation. This should not be sprayed unless you wear a respirator. Carbon arcs often used as a source of ultraviolet light, produce highly toxic ozone, nitrogen oxides and carbon monoxide, as well as UV light. They should not be used. Old hypo solutions produce highly toxic sulfur dioxide gas.

Stained Glass

One of the main hazards in stained glasswork is lead poisoning. I know of several diagnosed and suspected lead poisoning cases among stained glass workers—both among those using lead came and those using the copper foil technique. Both techniques involve soldering with lead/tin solders and there is the danger of inhaling the lead solder fumes, especially if the solder (and lead came) are overheated, as can happen with torches or overly powered electric soldering irons. In addition the settled lead fumes can coat surfaces and be transferred to hands and to the mouth. Since the copper foil technique uses large amounts of solder, this technique can involve an even greater risk. With lead came, there is the additional risk of inhalation or accidental ingestion of lead dust from cutting or sanding the lead came. This can be particularly a hazard if you eat, drink or smoke while working, or don't wash up carefully after work. Remember that other family members can also be at risk if you work at home. Recently a four-year-old boy developed lead poisoning as a result of being present when his parents were doing their stained glass in the kitchen.

Acid fluxes (zinc chloride, muriatic acid) can cause skin burns. In addition the fumes are strong lung irritants and can cause pulmonary edema if large amounts are inhaled at any one time. A more likely possibility is the development of chronic bronchitis or emphysema from repeated inhalation of smaller amounts of the fumes. The fumes from other fluxes are also irritating to the lungs, but to a lesser extent.

Hydrofluoric acid used for glass etching is highly poisonous. It can cause very severe and painful burns, especially under the fingernails. One problem is that there is no burning sensation until several hours after exposure. Inhalation causes severe respiratory irritation and possible pulmonary edema. It can also affect the bones and teeth. Remember, when diluting hydrofluoric acid always add acid to water.

Stained glass can involve many other techniques to color and decorate the glass. Many of these chemicals are highly hazardous, especially if sprayed onto hot glass. Many different patinas are used on the lead came. Copper sulfate is highly toxic by ingestion; skin contact may cause dermatitis and inhalation may cause perforation of the nasal septum and congestion. Antimony trichloride (butter of antimony) is highly corrosive to the skin and respiratory system. Antimony poisoning often resembles arsenic poisoning. Silver nitrate is moderately corrosive to skin and respiratory system. Selenium dioxide, sometimes used as a patina, is a skin irritant. In combination with strong acid it can produce the highly poisonous gas hydrogen selenide.

Commercial Art

Commercial art includes such techniques as drawing, painting, retouching and paste-up of mechanicals. A wide variety of materials are used including paints, dyes, inks, bleaches, spray fixatives and adhesives, rubber cement, solvents, etc. which can be applied by pen, brush, swab, felt marker, aerosol spray can or air brush.

Rubber cement and rubber cement thinner used for paste-up usually contain large amounts of the extremely flammable and highly toxic hexane. Hexane can cause dermatitis, narcosis from inhalation of large amounts at any one time, and peripheral neuropathy (inflammation and possible paralysis of arms and legs) from chronic inhalation of large amounts. In many cases, rubber cement can be replaced by wax as an adhesive. Otherwise good ventilation is needed.

Paints can be either water-based (water color, acrylic, gouache) or solvent or oil-based (oil, alkyd, lacquer). With water-based paints the only concern is with the pigments, as discussed under PAINTING. When painting with a brush, one is concerned about accidental ingestion or getting the paint in cuts. With air brush, pigments can be inhaled, which is much more hazardous, especially with highly toxic pigments like chrome yellow, zinc yellow, cadmium and manganese colors. When air brushing water-based paints, you need a respirator with a paint spray filter. For paints which use solvents, the hazards of solvent inhalation is found with both brush painting and air brush, although air brush is more hazardous because you are inhaling liquid droplets. In this case you need a respirator with organic vapor cartridge and spray prefilter, or if possible a spray booth. The use of solvents for cleaning also requires ventilation.

Dyes are used in felt markers, colored inks, spray markers and liquid water colors such as Dr. PH Martin's and Luma brands. The hazards of most of these dyes are unknown since few long term toxicity studies have been carried out. They can be water- based (liquid water colors, water-soluble felt markers) or solvent -based (permanent markers, spray markers, many colored inks). A wide variety of solvents are used, but the highly toxic aromatic hydrocarbons such as toluene and xylene are among the most common. These require very good ventilation. If the dyes are sprayed, then a spray booth or respirator with a spray prefilter and an organic vapor cartridge (for solvent types) is essential. The use of bleaches to remove the dyes from the skin is not recommended since the bleach can cause dermatitis. It is better to avoid skin contact in the first place, for example through the use of barrier creams or gloves, if possible.

Spray fixatives and spray adhesives are commonly used in commercial art. They are very toxic by inhalation due to the presence of solvents and adhesive or fixative. Toluene, chlorinated hydrocarbons and petroleum distillates are very common as solvents. Petroleum distillates are not usually considered highly toxic unless they contain hexane, but in spray mist form they may cause pulmonary edema and pneumonia if substantial quantities enter the lungs. The long term hazards of the adhesive and fixative are not known. However, hairdressers who use aerosol sprays regularly have been found to have a higher rate of chronic lung problems than the rest of the population. In addition aerosol spray cans are explosive and usually flammable. The replacement of freons by extremely flammable gases like propane has caused a great increase in the number of fires in the last couple of years. Whenever possible aerosol sprays should be replaced by non-aerosol products. Mouth atomizers for spraying are not recommended because of the risk of back-up of the liquid into the mouth.

Retouching of drawings, packages, photographs, etc. is another common commercial art technique. It uses all of the materials described above, as well as other materials specific for retouching. This is particularly true for photographic retouching. Freon and methyl chloroform (1,1,1-trichloroethane) are commonly used for film cleaning. Freon is only slightly toxic although in large quantities it may cause irregularities in heart rhythms. Methyl chloroform is one of the least toxic chlorinated hydrocarbons although it can cause narcosis and also has been implicated in heart problems.

Iodine and potassium iodide in water is commonly used as a black and white bleach. Iodine is a strong skin irritant and is poisonous if ingested. Ethyl alcohol, which is only slightly toxic, is used as a stopping agent, and thiourea as a clearing agent. Thiourea is suspect as a cancer agent in humans since it causes cancer in animals.

A variety of chemicals are used for color bleaching. One of the commonest is potassium permanganate in diluted nitric or sulfuric acids. Sodium bisulfite is the clearing agent. Potassium permanganate is highly corrosive as the powder or concentrated solutions, and mildly irritating in dilute solution. Nitric and sulfuric acids are also highly corrosive in concentrated solution. When diluting these acids, always add the acid to the water, never the reverse. Wear rubber gloves and goggles. Sodium bisulfite decomposes in acid solutions to produce sulfur dioxide which is highly irritating to the eyes, nose and respiratory system.

In transparency retouching, potassium permanganate, sulfuric acid and sodium chloride or Chloramine-T and acetic acid are used to bleach yellow dyes. Do not add more potassium permanganate solution than specified in directions because of the danger of producing highly toxic chlorine gas. Similarly Chloramine-T releases chlorine gas in acid solutions. The Chloramine-T powder is also irritating to the skin, eyes, nose and respiratory system. Use of all of the above bleaches requires local exhaust ventilation.

Stannous chloride and disodium EDTA is used as a magenta dye bleach. Stannous chloride solutions are skin irritants and the dust is a respiratory irritant. Disodium EDTA is highly toxic by ingestion, causing kidney damage and tetany (irregular muscular spasms of the extremities) due to calcium depletion. Sodium hydrosulfite (sodium dithionite) used in a cyan bleach is flammable and can decompose to produce sulfur dioxide. Sodium cyanide is occasionally used as a bleach. Sodium cyanide causes skin rashes and is extremely toxic by ingestion and possibly by inhalation. It causes chemical asphyxia. Sodium cyanide reacts with acids to produce the poison gas hydrogen cyanide. This can even happen in aqueous solution due to carbon dioxide in the air. Preferably do not use cyanide bleach. If you must, do so only in a fume hood and have a cyanide antidote kit available at all times.

Gum arabic solution is often sprayed onto photographs as a fixative. Inhalation of gum arabic can cause "printers' asthma," so-called because about 50% of the printers who used to spray it developed asthma.

Children and Art Materials

Despite the concern over lead poisoning in children and attempts to eliminate children's exposure to such lead-containing materials as wall paints and pencils, many children are still being exposed to lead in art classes in schools, community centers and even the home. One of the authors (M.R.), for example, has observed situations in which children were using raw lead glazes, lead frits and lead enamels. Many people mistakenly assume that lead frits are "safe", whereas in actuality many commercial lead frits can dissolve in stomach acids. Other sources of lead in art materials sometimes used with children include silkscreen and other printmaking inks, lead solders and stained glass. Recent examples of lead poisoning in children include a child swallowing stencil paint which upon analysis was found to contain at least 30 percent lead, and a four-year-old boy developing lead poisoning after being present in the kitchen where his parents were involved in stained glass work. One of the problems is that these materials usually do not state that they contain lead nor do they carry warning labels.

Lead, however, isn't the only hazardous art material being used by chidren. For example, ingestion of one tablespoon of turpentine can be fatal to a child, and ingestion of two tablespoons of methyl alcohol (found in many shellacs) could have serious toxic effects, possibly including blindness. Other art materials that are toxic by single or repeated ingestions of small amounts include many solvents (paint thinner, kerosene, lacquer thinners, etc.), acids, alkalis, photographic chemicals, dyes and many pottery glaze ingredients.

Ingestion, however, is not the only way in which art materials can injure children. Skin contact with many art materials can cause burns, irritation, ulcers and allergies. Examples include solvents which defat the skin, acids and alkalis which can cause severe burns, formaldehyde and turpentine which can cause skin allergies, and potassium dichromate (a natural dye mordant) which can cause skin and nose ulcers. If the skin has cuts or sores, then many toxic materials can enter the body through these breaks in the skin's defences. In addition many solvents can be absorbed through the skin into the body.

Finally, inhalation of solvent vapors, dusts, aerosol spray mists and metal fumes can either injure the lungs or be absorbed through the lungs into the bloodstream. Common art materials containing hazardous solvents include turpentine, paint thinner, paint and varnish removers, rubber cement, silk screen inks and solvents, lacquers and their thinners, shellac, permanent markers, cleaning solvents, aerosol spray cans and solvent-based glues and adhesives. Hazardous dusts include asbestos, dry clay, glaze ingredients, dye powders, tempera powders, plaster dust and sawdust. Other toxic art materials children may be exposed to include etching gases, kiln gases, soldering fumes, and gases from photographic developing.

What Is the Risk?

We believe that children under the age of about 12 should not be exposed to most hazardous materials. This conclusion is based on both physiological and psychological reasons.

First, children are at much higher risk physiologically than adults from exposure to toxic materials. There are several reasons for this. Children and teenagers are still growing and have a more rapid metabolism than adults. As a result they are more likely to absorb toxic materials into their bodies. With young children this can especially affect the brain and nervous system. Young children also have incompletely developed lungs and body defences and are therefore particularly more susceptible to inhalation hazards. Finally, children are at higher risk because of their smaller body weight. A certain amount of toxic material is more concentrated in a child's body than it is in a larger adult body. Therefore, the smaller the child, the greater the risk.

Second, children under the age of 12 cannot be depended upon to either understand the need to carry out precautions or to effectively carry them out on a consistent basis. Preschool children are likely to deliberately put things in their mouth and swallow them, thus creating an even greater hazard. Even though older children might not deliberately swallow art materials, there have been several fatalities due to accidentally swallowing turpentine or paint thinner that had been carelessly stored in soda bottles, orange juice containers or similar containers. In addition accidental ingestion can occur by placing contaminated hands in the mouth.

For these reasons, we recommend that

children under the age of 12 not be allowed to use art materials that are hazardous by ingestion, skin contact or inhalation. Junior and senior high school students, although they are still at higher risk than adults, are at an age where they might normally be expected to understand the need for precautions and to consistently carry out precautions. Of course this generalization has exceptions, particularly with retarded or rebellious students. However, we would still recommend that even junior and senior high school students should not use highly toxic materials like asbestos, lead, mercury and cadmium, since even small exposures to these materials can have severe effects.

What Art Materials Should Children Use?

Many art materials recommended in children's art books are highly toxic and should not be used by children. For example, one state curriculum guide for art in elementary schools recommends the use of benzene and carbon tetrachloride—both extremely toxic solvents—for clean-up, and also contains a recipe for a clay substitute that calls for "three cups of ground asbestos." The use of these materials is even hazardous to the teachers.

This brings up the question of how can you tell which art materials are safe or how can children work with them safely? Many children's art materials have a label stating they are "non-toxic." Unfortunately this label can be misleading since many children's art materials have not been tested for long term toxicity, including possible cancer. Further most art material manufacturers do not have toxicologists or other personnel competent to evaluate the hazards of the materials they are using. The only program we know of which has attempted to ensure the safety of children's art materials is that of the Crayon, Watercolor and Craft Institute. Art materials carrying their Certified Product (CP) or Approved Product (AP) seal of approval have been "certified by an authority of toxicology, associated with a leading university, to contain no materials in sufficient quantities to be toxic or injurious to the body, even if ingested."

The following are some recommendations for the use of art materials with children:
• Do not allow children to use adult art materials containing toxic solvents, dusts, metals, acids, alkalis, etc.
• Use water-based art materials such as water-based inks, paints, and glues. Make sure that print-making inks, paints, etc. do not contain lead, chromium, cadmium or other toxic pigments. Do not use epoxy, instant glues or solvent-based adhesives such as rubber cement.
• Some art techniques can be used with children if hazardous steps are done by the teacher when children are not present. For examples, the mixing of clay, plaster and other powders with water, spray fixing drawings and clean-up with hazardous solvents should be done by the teachers.
• Clean the art area carefully so that toxic dusts such as clay, plaster, etc., do not accumulate where they can be inhaled by children (or teacher).
• Do not allow food or drink in the art area because of the risk of contamination and make sure children wash their hands carefully after class. Make sure children do not have exposed cuts or sores on their hands.
• Ventilate all kilns, including electric kilns.

Safety in the Studio

Less Toxic Materials

One of the best ways to decrease or eliminate a health hazard is to find a less toxic substitute. In particular, benzol, carbon tetrachloride and asbestos are so highly toxic that it is extremely difficult for most artists to work safely with these materials. So substitutes should be found wherever they are used. This rule is true in general of all materials that can cause cancer, since there is evidence that there is no safe level of exposure to a carcinogen. However, the rule can also be extended to other materials. Whenever you can choose a less toxic solvent in preference to one that is more toxic, for example, you are substantially decreasing possible health hazards.

Often you can use less hazardous techniques. For example, use ready-made paints rather than mixing your own and handling toxic dusts which can be inhaled, or use wet grinding techniques rather than dry grinding techniques.

Ventilation

One of the most important factors in designing a studio—and one of the most neglected—is adequate ventilation. There are two types of ventilation. Local or exhaust ventilation, removes toxic vapors, dusts, etc. at their source before they can contaminate the air and people's breathing zones. General or dilution ventilation dilutes the toxic vapors with fresh air to lower their concentration to a safer level. Obviously, therefore, the first method is preferred.

Local ventilation is particularly important in situations where highly toxic materials or large amounts of toxic materials are being produced. Examples are welding, carbon arcs, acid baths for etching (particularly with nitric acid), silk screen drying and wash-up, spraying operations, grinding and sanding, and processes producing asbestos-containing dusts.

A local exhaust system consists of an exhaust hood to trap the contaminant, a duct system to carry the contaminant to the outside, an exhaust fan and sometimes, air-cleaning equipment to prevent the toxic materials from polluting the atmosphere.

There are many factors that affect the design and placement of an exhaust hood. First, the shape of the hood greatly affects its efficiency. Since the hood opening draws in air from all directions, enclosing the operation so that air is drawn only from the direction desired means that less air is required. For example, the flanges on the end of the movable duct for exhaust welding fumes (figure 1) prevent the air from behind the duct from entering the duct. Similarly the spray booth type of hood (figure 2) encloses the spraying operation so that the exhaust fan is only exhausting air that is contaminated with spray. Note the baffles in the spray booth which ensure an even distribution of air and also catch much of the liquid so that the fan doesn't get clogged.

Second, the hood should be located so that the natural velocity of the contaminant will be in the direction of the hood opening. For example, the exhaust duct of the spray booth in figure 2 is at the rear of the booth because that is the direction in which the spray is aimed. Similarly, since hot fumes rise, the use of updrafts for carbon arcs

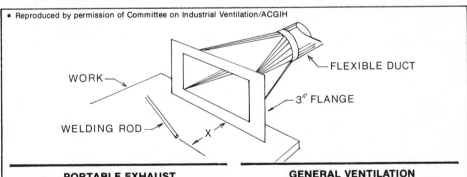

WORK

FLEXIBLE DUCT

3″ FLANGE

WELDING ROD

X

PORTABLE EXHAUST		
x inches	Plain duct cfm	Flange or Cone cfm
up to 6	335	250
6-9	755	560
9-12	1335	1000

Face velocity—1500 fpm
Duct velocity—3000 fpm minimum
Entry loss—0.25 duct VP

GENERAL VENTILATION where local exhaust cannot be used	
Rod diam	cfm/welder*
5/32	1000
3/16	1500
1/4	3500
3/8	4500

*For toxic materials higher airflows are necessary and operator may require respiratory protection equipment

FIG. 1 Portable local exhaust hood for welding

23

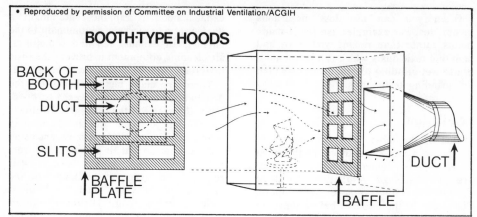

BOOTH·TYPE HOODS

BACK OF BOOTH

DUCT

SLITS

BAFFLE PLATE

DUCT

BAFFLE

FIG. 2 Diagrammatic representation of a ventilated spraying booth

takes advantage of this natural tendency. Most carbon arcs are equipped with attachments for overhead flexible ducts. Also, since solvent vapors are not heavier than air, they do not fall and exhaust inlets should be at the level the vapors are produced.

Third, the hood should be placed as close as possible to the source of the contaminant. As shown in figure 3, the velocity of the exhaust drops off very sharply as the distance from the hood increases. To trap a contaminant and direct it into the hood, the air velocity at the source of contamination must be greater than the natural velocity of the contamin-

ant and surrounding air. The further away the hood is, the more powerful the fan will have to be to achieve this capture velocity at the source of contamination.

Fourth, care should be taken in designing and locating the hood so that contaminants do not pass through peoples' breathing zones before being trapped by the hood. This would negate the whole purpose of the local exhaust system.

Finally, make sure that you have provided for an adequate source of make-up air to replace the air entering the hood. Otherwise the system does not work.

The duct system should be made of materials that won't be affected by the

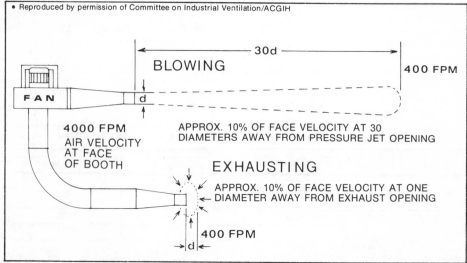

30d

BLOWING

400 FPM

FAN

d

4000 FPM
AIR VELOCITY
AT FACE
OF BOOTH

APPROX. 10% OF FACE VELOCITY AT 30
DIAMETERS AWAY FROM PRESSURE JET OPENING

EXHAUSTING

APPROX. 10% OF FACE VELOCITY AT ONE
DIAMETER AWAY FROM EXHAUST OPENING

400 FPM

d

FIG. 3 Local exhaust system with simple duct openings. Shows effect of distance on air velocity.

contaminant. For example, if you are exhausting organic solvents, the ducts should be fire-proof. To keep air flowing smoothly, ducts should be circular with as few bends as possible, and those bends should be gradual. With dusts, duct air velocity should be sufficient to keep dusts from settling.

The type and capacity of the fan to be used depends on the contaminant and the required air velocity. For gases and solvent vapors, propeller fans are sufficient. When exhausting solvents, the fan must be explosion-proof. For more details, refer to "Industrial Ventilation—A Manual of Recommended Practice" (see References).

General ventilation is used commonly to heat or cool the air to make it comfortable. But it can also be used to provide the make-up air for a local exhaust system and to bring in fresh air from outside to dilute the concentration of a toxic material to a safer level. In the first case, a recirculating type of system is common (e.g., air conditioner), but in some cases a recirculating system will actually build up the concentration of toxic materials.

A general ventilation system usually consists of air inlets and outlets, blowers, exhaust fans and ducting. Often, an open door or other source of comfortable make-up air and a window exhaust fan of appropriate capacity are adequate.

In designing a dilution ventilation system, there are several factors to consider. First, make sure that there is enough make-up air entering the room to replace that being exhausted. Second, make sure that the air inlet and outlet are sufficiently far apart that there is no chance of contaminated air from the outlet getting back in. Third, design the air flow so that it reaches people before being contaminated. Finally, make sure that the air is evenly distributed throughout the room and that there are no uncomfortable drafts.

The actual flow rate of air needed to dilute a contaminant to a safe level depends on the toxicity of the material, the amount of material escaping into the air, and the period of time over which this occurs. This can be calculated since all the above variables are known or can be measured.

Finally the ventilation system—whether local or general—should be regularly checked to see if it is operating correctly.

Flammable Solvents

The storage and handling of flammable solvents is usually regulated by the Fire Department. These regulations vary from city to city. New York City has one of the strictest fire prevention codes in the country. For example, in New York you need a fire permit to store or use more than five gallons of a flammable solvent; welders also require a fire permit.

The flammability of a solvent is determined mostly by its *flash point*, which is the lowest temperature at which a liquid gives off enough vapors to form an ignitable mixture with air, and can cause a flame to form when a source of ignition is present. This source of ignition can be a flame, a lit cigarette, a spark, static electricity, etc. The National Fire Protection Association, in its NFPA Standard #30, *Flammable and Combustible Liquids Code*, classifies liquids as flammable if their flash point is below 100° F, and as combustible if the flash point is above 100° F. Flammable liquids are subdivided into Classes 1A, 1B and 1C, and combustible liquids are subdivided into Classes II and III.

As Table II (page 26) shows, many of the common solvents are highly flammable *at room temperatures*. In addition mixtures are often as flammable as the most flammable component since one component catching fire can set off the other components.

The fire hazard warnings on art materials you buy in stores are defined by the Federal Hazardous Substances Act, not the NFPA. According to this Act, a liquid is *extremely flammable* if its flash point is below 20 degrees F (e.g. acetone), is *flammable* if its flash point is above 20 degrees F but below 80 degrees F, and is *combustible* if its flash point is at or above 80 degrees but below 150 degrees F. The main difference between definitions occurs with liquids having flash points between 80 degrees F and 100 degrees F. According to NFPA #30, they are flammable Class 1C, but by the Federal Hazardous Substances Act they are combustible. Common liquids used by artists and craftspeople in this

Table II—Flashpoints of Common Solvents

	NFPA Class	Flash Point	Examples
Flammable	IA	under 73° F (boiling pt. under 100° F)	ethyl ether, "flammable" aerosol sprays
	IB	under 73° F (boiling pt. 100° F or over)	acetone, benzol, benzine, ethyl acetate, ethyl alcohol, ethylene dichloride, gasoline, hexane, isopropyl alcohol, methanol, methyl ethyl ketone, petroleum naphtha, toluene
	IC	73-100° F	butyl alcohol, methyl isobutyl ketone, propyl alcohol, styrene, turpentine, xylene
Combustible	II	100-140° F	cellosolve acetate, isoamyl alcohol, acetic acid, kerosene, Stoddard solvent, mineral spirits

category are turpentine, xylol (xylene), styrene (found in polyester resins), and some components of lacquer thinners. My opinion is that the definitions used in NFPA #30 are more useful, and you should consider these liquids flammable. A further difference between the two sets of regulations is that only Class II liquids are considered combustible by the Hazardous Substances Control Act, and not Class III liquids.

Particular care should be taken with Class I and II solvents. More than one quart should not be stored in open or glass containers, but in approved safety containers. Containers with screw lids are not good because they can't release built-up pressure. Waste flammable liquids should similarly be stored in approved safety-type disposal cans which are emptied each day. Large quantities of flammable liquids should be stored in approved storage cabinets.

Another essential in a studio or workshop is a readily available fire extinguisher (or fire extinguishers). If you are using flammable solvents you should get a Class B (flammable liquid) fire extinguisher. The best type is a dry chemical or carbon dioxide extinguisher.

Handling and Housekeeping Precautions

The following are a set of precautions to use in handling and cleaning up of toxic art materials.

1. *Read labels careully.* Warnings and precautions on the labels of art materials usually satisfy the minimum requirements of law. Unfortunately, even these legal minimums are often not met.

2. *Store materials safely.* Label all containers and preferably use metal or plastic containers rather than breakable glass containers. Do not use coke bottles, milk cartons, etc. which might tempt a child to drink the contents or which adults might even drink by accident. Cover all containers when not in use—even if only for a minute.

3. *Use proper personal hygiene precautions.* Don't eat or smoke in the studio because of the danger of accidental ingestion. Wash off splashes immediately with lots of water. In case of eye splashes, rinse eyes for at least 15 minutes and call a doctor. Wash hands with soap and water or a safe waterless hand cleanser (no solvents, alkali or harsh abrasives). Never use solvents to wash hands.

If you live and work in the same space, a separate area should be set aside for working. Work clothes should be washed separate from other clothes to avoid contamination.

4. *Watch out for physical hazards.* Tie back you hair and do not wear loose clothing, ties, beads, etc., which might get caught in moving parts of machinery. When using sharp tools, cut away from you and put your free hand behind or to the side of the tool, not in front. Make sure all electrical equipment is adequately grounded and that the wiring is in good repair.

5. *Clean up all spills immediately.* For liquids use paper towels, rags or newspaper and store in waste disposal cans which are emptied every day. If the spill is large and the liquid hazardous by inhalation, wear a respirator. Similar procedures should be used in cleaning up with solvents, for example, in silk screen wash-up.

In cleaning up dusts, *never sweep.* This just stirs up the dust so you inhale it. Instead use vacuuming or wet mopping (or both). Very toxic dusts (e.g., asbestos-containing dusts) should be vacuumed with industrial-type vacuum cleaners into special single-use bags that can be removed and sealed. Dust is a problem in particular in wood-carving and sanding, stonework, pottery, clay and plaster modeling, and some plastic work.

6. *Dispose of hazardous chemicals safely.* The best way to dispose of small amounts of solvents, according to the Environmental Protection Agency, is to let them evaporate. This should only be done in a fume hood or similar safe method to avoid inhalation of these solvents. Large amounts of solvents should be disposed of through a waste disposal service, not the garbage can. If you must pour chemicals down the sink (e.g. acids, water solutions, water-soluble solutions), so do slowly flushing at the same time with lots of water. Do not mix chemicals since this might cause the formation of toxic gases or might cause explosions or fire in some instances.

Personal Protective Equipment

Respirators

The Occupational Safety and Health Act of 1970 states that in industry, respirators are allowed only for emergency use, when local exhaust ventilation is not possible, or as a temporary measure while local exhaust systems are being installed. This is a good rule for anybody to follow, since local exhaust systems are more efficient and safer than respirators. Respirators are also uncomfortable to wear over extended periods of time. Further, since respirators are difficult to breathe through, people with heart or breathing difficulties should consult their doctor before buying a respirator.

Respirators are of two basic types: air-supplying and air-purifying. Air-supplying respirators provide a source of uncontaminated air for the person to breathe. The air can come from a self-contained breathing apparatus (SCBE) separate tanks of compressed air or from a compressor. This type of respirator is fairly expensive and needed only in cases of oxygen deficiency or with materials that are immediately harmful to life or health. In this category I would include welding with toxic metals or fluoride fluxes, spraying with polyurethane foam and processes producing asbestos dust.

Air-purifying respirators, on the other hand, remove the toxic materials from the air you are breathing. These include full gas masks, covering the entire face, and half-masks, covering the mouth, nose and often chin. These respirators consist of two basic parts: the face mask, and the cartridge, canister or filter which removes the contaminant. There are different cartridges and filters for different contaminants. A cartridge or filter intended for one contaminant will not work for other types. There are separate cartridges available for organic vapors (silk screening, solvents, plastics casting and molding, etc.); for acid gases (nitric acid etching—use full face gas mask—and for hydrocholoric acid etching) and for carbon monoxide (in foundries)—use full face gas mask. There are also different filters for dusts, fumes and mists. Filters should be used only for purposes specified, e.g., dusts (sculpture, ceramics, pigments); fumes (condensed metal vapors, especially in welding and foundry work) or mists (paint and other sprays). Combinations of cartridges and filters and combinations of different types of cartridges are also available.

In choosing a respirator, there are several factors to take into account. First, the respirator should have a NIOSH (National Institute of Occupational Safety and Health) approval. These approvals are good only if the respirator is used for the purpose stated on the approval. Do not use nuisance or non-toxic dust masks for protection against toxic materials.

Second, the respirator you choose should fit properly. If air can leak in around the edges, it is worse than useless, since you will have a false sense of security. People have differently shaped faces, so a respirator that fits one person will not necessarily fit someone else. If it doesn't fit, try another size or model. To test the fit, close off the intake valves and breathe in. No air should leak in. Another test is to close the outlet valve and breathe out. No air should escape.

Finally the respirator you choose should fit comfortably. If it doesn't, you will find that you often won't wear it when you should.

Air-purifying respirators normally cost about $10-$15. Air-supplied types are much more expensive.

Cartridges and filters have to be changed regularly. The purifying chemicals in cartridges eventually get used up and vapors or gases start to enter the mask. The time this takes depends on the frequency and length of use and level of exposure. With many contaminants, you can go by odor. However, with odorless or highly toxic gases, use full face mask or air-supplying respirator. Filters get clogged, which is easy to tell by the increased difficulty in breathing.

Respirators should be regularly checked for damage, cleaned and disinfected. One recommended cleaning procedure follows:

1) Remove filters, cartridges, or canisters.
2) Wash face piece and any tubing in soap and water using a handbrush to remove dirt.

3) Rinse completely in warm water.
4) Air dry in a *clean* area. Don't heat.
5) Clean other parts as recommended by manufacturer.
6) Inspect head-straps, valves, etc. and replace with new parts if needed.
7) Insert cartridge, canister or filter, making sure there is a tight seal.
8) Place in a plastic bag or container for storage. The respirator should never be stored near chemicals, heat, light, dust.

For further information concerning respirators, consult the American National Standards Institute booklet, *Practices for Respiratory Protection*, ANSI Z88.2-1969, available from ANSI at 1430 Broadway, New York, NY 10018.

Skin Protection

Dermatitis is one of the biggest dangers of working with art materials. The best way to prevent dermatitis is to prevent toxic material from contacting your skin, particularly your hands. The best way to do this is to wear plastic or rubber gloves, especially when working with organic solvents, acids and caustics. There are two basic requirements in choosing the type of glove: first, that the glove is impervious to the materials being used; and, second, that the glove allow the degree of "feel" required for your art.

Different types of gloves will protect against different solvents. Latex/neoprene gloves are effective against most solvents, although they might not last as long with aromatic and chlorinated hydrocarbons (e.g. toluene, xylene, paint and varnish removers, lacquer thinners, polyester resin, methylene chloride, etc). Neoprene rubber does not protect against aromatic hydrocarbons, nor does butyl rubber against aromatic hydrocarbons and petroleum distillates, nor does NBR rubber against chlorinated hydrocarbons and ketones. Latex or natural rubber should only be used for protection against dilute acids, alkalis, alcohols and ketones. Polyvinyl chloride ("vinyl") gloves only protect against alcohols, dilute acids, alkalis, and most other water-based materials. Most gloves can be used to protect against paints, grease and other non-solvent materials.

The actual life of a glove depends on use

conditions, including length of contact with the chemicals, temperature, concentration of liquid, and physical wear and tear. For example your gloves will last longer when used to protect against solvent-soaked rags than against dipping in pure solvent for extended periods. You can also prolong the life of your gloves by washing them with soap and water before removing them and then allowing them to air dry.

If you cannot wear gloves, then the use of barrier creams ("invisible gloves") might help, by providing an impermeable barrier between the skin and toxic material. There are different types of barrier creams, some water-soluble and other water-insoluble. Silicone types are supposed to be best. (See appendix for list of companies). These barrier creams have to be renewed regularly. After use, the barrier creams are washed off with a mild soap and water.

In cleaning hands, it is important to wash carefully and frequently with soap and water (especially before eating, smoking, etc.). Do not use harsh or abrasive soaps, since these can cause dermatitis themselves and just increase the problem. With some materials, including paints, ink, oils, etc. waterless hand cleansers are helpful. They are often available in hardware and art supply stores. Cleansers containing kerosene are not recommended because of their defatting action. After washing with these cleansers, you should also wash with plenty of soap and water. Then use a hand lotion or cream containing lanolin to replace any skin oils lost.

Face and Eye Protection

The face and eyes must be protected against a variety of hazards, including impact (chipping, grinding,etc.), radiation (welding, carbon arcs, foundries) and chemical splash (acids, caustics, etc.). Safety equipment that is chosen to protect against a particular hazard should state that it meets the standards ot the American National Standards Institute's *Practice for Occupational and Educational Eye and Face Protection,* (ANSI publication Z87.1).

Protection against impact is of three types: spectacles with impact-resistant lenses and side shields, flexible or cushioned goggles, and chipping or eyecup goggles. Models are available that can be worn with or without glasses. For some types of exposure, a combination of goggles and face shield is advised.

The type of protection against radiation depends on the type of radiation to which you are exposed. Carbon arcs and electric welding require protection against ultraviolet, visible and infared light. The latter two are felt as heat, In oxyacetylene and foundry work with molten metal the concern is mostly with protection against the visible and infared light. The type and degree of filtering needed in lenses will depend on these factors. Welding masks often cover the entire face to also protect the skin.

Protection against chemical splash depends on the severity of the problem. For work with hot, concentrated acids in large amounts, complete acid hoods covering head and shoulders are available. In other cases face shields or simply chemical goggles with baffled ventilation are sufficient. If you are working with irritating vapors, you might choose goggles without ventilation. In any case, if you get anything in your eyes, wash with lots of water for about fifteen minutes and consult a doctor immediately.

Other Protective Clothing

Protective clothing is also available to protect other parts of the body besides the skin, face and eyes. Normal clothing is effective against ultraviolet and visible light, but heat is another matter. Leather aprons or clothing usually give good protection. This includes leather gloves for handling hot objects. In some cases, asbestos gloves might be necessary. Leather clothing also gives protection against limited impact, including molten metal and sparks. In some cases protective shoes and hats might be needed.

For protection against chemical splash, plastic or cloth aprons are available in a variety of materials. In addition you can buy protective leggings and sleeves.

Ear Protection

Excessive noise can have both temporary and permanent effects on the body. This includes not only hearing losses, but also heart disease, gastrointestinal disorders, allergies, etc. Noise levels are measured in decibels (dB) on a logarithmic scale such that every increase of 10dB means that the noise intensity has increased tenfold. The table below lists the noise levels of some activities.

Table III—Noise Levels

ordinary conversation:	60dB
grinding:	80-89 dB
spraying	80-89 dB
machine shop:	80-89 dB
pneumatic drill:	90-99 dB
foundry operation:	90-99 dB
circular saw:	100-109 dB
woodworking shop:	110 dB

The Occupational Safety and Health Administration (OSHA) has set a maximum permissible noise level of 90 dB for an eight-hour working day. Many doctors think that this level is much too high.

The best way to solve excessive noise problems is to eliminate them at their source, just like the best way to control toxic materials is by local exhaust ventilation. Eliminating noise can be done in a variety of ways, including keeping machines in good repair, oiling where needed, mounting on rubber or other absorbent materials to reduce vibration, use of silencers and mufflers, etc. In addition there is the possibility of buying quieter machines.

If the above methods fail to work, then you can use ear muffs or ear plugs. Ear plugs come in a variety of sizes and types. Some of the new foam ear plugs are as effective as ear muffs. The use of improvised materials like wax or cotton is not recommended and may be harmful.

■

Appendix: Sources of Safety Equipment

NIOSH-Approved Respirators

American Optical Corp.
Safety Products Div.
100 Canal Street
Putman, CT 06260

Binks Manufacturing Co.
9201 W. Belmont Ave.
Franklin Park, IL 60131

Cesco Safety Products
Parmalee Industries Inc.
PO Box 1237
Kansas City, MO 64141

H.S. Cover Co.
107 East Alexander St.
Buchanan, MI 49107

DeVilbiss Co.
300 Phillips Ave.
P.O. Box 913
Toledo, OH 43692

Eastern Safety Equipment Co.
45-17 Pearson St.
Long Island City, NY 11101

Glendale Optical Co.
130 Crossways Park Drive
Woodbury, NY 11797

Mine Safety Appliances Co.
600 Penn Center Blvd.
Pittsburgh, PA 15235

Pulmosan Safety Equipment Corp.
30-48 Linden Place
Flushing, NY 11354

Safeline Products
P.O. Box 550
Putnam, CT 06260

Scott Aviation
Division of ATO, Inc.
Lancaster, NY 14086

3M Company
3M Center,
St. Paul, MN 55101

Sellstrom Manufacturing Co.
59 E. Van Buren St.
Chicago, IL 60605

United States Safety Service
P.O. Box 1237
Kansas City, MO 64141

Welsh Manufacturing Co.
9 Magnolia St.
Providence, RI 02909

Willson Products Div., ESB, Inc.
Box 622
Reading, PA 19603

Gloves and Other Protective Equipment

Cadillac Plastic and Chemical Co.
15841 2nd Avenue
Detroit, MI 48203

Curtin Matheson Scientific, Inc.
357 Hamburg Turnpike
Wayne, NJ 07470

Edmont-Wilson
Coshocton, OH 43812

Fisher Scientific Co.
711 Forbes Ave.
Pittsburgh, PA 15219

General Scientific Equipment Co.
Limekiln Pike and William Ave.
Philadelphia, PA 19151

Industrial Gloves Division
International Playtex Corp.
888 7th Avenue
New York, NY 10019

Kerodex Products, Averst Labs
685 Third Ave.
New York, NY 10017

Magid Glove Mfg. Co.
2060 N. Kolmar Ave.
Chicago, IL 60639

Milburn Co.
3246 E. Woodbridge
Detroit, MI 48207

Mine Safety Appliances Co.
600 Penn Center Blvd.
Pittsburgh, PA 15235

Many of the above-mentioned companies have local sales offices in major cities. In addition, check under safety equipment in your yellow pages.

Bibliography

General References

American Mutual Insurance Alliance: *Handbook of Organic Industrial Solvents* 4th edition, Chicago (1972)

American National Standards Institute: *Practice for Occupational and Educational Eye and Face Protection.* ANSI Z87.1-1968, New York (1968)

American National Standards Institute: *Practices for Respiratory Protection.* ANSI Z88.2-1969, New York (1969)

Committee on Industrial Ventilation: *Industrial Ventilation—A Manual of Recommended Practice*, 13th ed., American Conference of Governmental Industrial Hygienists, Cincinatti (1975)

Gleason, Marion *et al: Clinical Toxicology of Commerical Products.* 3rd Edition, Williams and Wilkins Co., Baltimore (1969)

Hamilton, Alice and H.L. Hardy: *Industrial Toxicology*, 3rd edition, Publishing Sciences Group, Inc., Acton (1974)

International Labor Organization: *Encyclopedia of Occupational Health and Safety*, McGraw-Hill, New York (1972)

The Merck Chemical Index of Chemicals and Drugs, 8th edition, Merck and Co., Rahway, NJ (1968)

National Fire Protection Association: *Flammable and Combustible Liquids Code* NFPA #30, Boston (1973)

National Institute of Occupational Safety Health: *The Industrial Environment—Its Evaluation and Control*, U.S. Government Printing Office, Washington (1973)

National Safety Council: *Accident Prevention Manual for Industrial Operations.* 6th ed., Chicago (1969)

Patty, Frank, (Ed.): *Industrial Hygiene and Toxicology*, Volume II, 2nd edition, Interscience Publishers, New York (1963)

Sax, N. Irving: *Dangerous Properties of Industrial Materials*, 4th edition, Van Nostrand Reinhold Company, New York (1975)

Stellman, Jeanne, and Susan Daum: *Work Is Dangerous To Your Health*, Vintage Paperbacks, New York (1973)

Art Hazards References

Agoston, George: "Health and Safety Hazards of Art Materials." *Leonardo.* 2: 373 (1969)

Alexander, W.: "Ceramic Toxicology." *Studio Potter.* p. 35 (Winter, 1973/74)

Barazani, Gail: "Protecting Your Health" column. *Working Craftsman.*

Barazani, Gail (editor): *Health Hazards in Art Newsletter I & II.* Hazards in Art, Chicago (1977)

Bond, Judith: "Occupational Hazards of Stained Glass Workers." *Glass Art. 4[1]:* 45 (1976)

Carnow, Bertram: "Health Hazards in the Arts." *American Lung Association Bulletin.* p.2 (January/February, 1976)

Carnow, Bertram: *Health Hazards in the Arts and Crafts.* Hazards in the Arts, Chicago (1975)

Dreggson, Alan: "Lead Poisoning." *Glass.* 5[2]: 13 (1977)

Feldman, R. and T. Sedman: "Hobbyists Working With Lead." *New England Journal of Medicine 292*: 929(1975)

Foote, Richard: "Health Hazards to Commercial Artists." *Job Safety and Health.* p.7 (November, 1977)

Halpern, Fay and Michael McCann: "Health Hazards Report: Caution with Dyes." *Craft Horizons*, p. 46 (August, 1976)

Jenkins, Catherine L.: "Textile Dyes Are Potential Hazards." *Journal of Environmental Health*, p. 18 (March/April, 1978)

Mallary, Robert: "The Air of Art Is Poisoned." *Art News*, p. 34 (October, 1963)

Index

McCann, Michael: "Health Hazards in Printmaking." *Print Review # 4*, p. 20 (1975)

McCann, Michael: "Health Hazards in Painting." *American Artist* p. 73 (February, 1976)

McCann, Michael: "Art Hazards News column." *Art Workers News*

McCann, Michael: "Health Hazards in the Arts and Crafts." Paper presented at 105th Annual Meeting of American Public Health Assoc. (November, 1977)

McCann, Michael: "The Impact of Hazards in Art on Female Workers." *Preventive Medicine* (September, 1978)

Moses, Cheries, James Purdham, Dwight Bowhay and Roland Hosein: *Health and Safety in Printmaking: a manual for printmakers.* Occupational Hygiene Branch, Alberta Labor, Edmonton, Alberta, Canada (1978)

Siedlicki, Jerome: "Occupational Health Hazards of Painters and Sculptors." *Journal of American Medical Association* 204: 1176 (1968)

Siedlicki, Jerome: "Potential Hazards of Plastics Used in Sculpture." *Art Education* (February, 1972)

Siedlicki, Jerome: *The Silent Enemy* 2nd ed., Artists' Equity Association, Washington (1975)

Stewart, R. and C. Hake: "Paint-Remover Hazard." *Journal of the American Medical Association 235*: 398 (1976)

Waller, Julian and Lawrence Whitehead: "Health Issues" column, *Craft Horizons*

Waller, Julian and Lawrence Whitehead (editors): *Health Hazards in the Arts— Proceedings of the 1977 Vermont Workshops.* University of Vermont Department of Epidemiology and Environmental Health, Burlington (1977)

Wellborn, Stanley: "Health Hazards in Woodworking." *Fine Woodworking* (Winter, 1977)

■ The index lists art materials, techniques, chemicals and occupational diseases, and the page numbers on which these references occur. Symptoms of diseases are not generally included in the index because symptoms are often very vague and apply to many different types of chemical poisonings.

A

acetates 7
acetic acid 2,3,7,17,18,20
acetone 6,7
acetylene tetrachloride, *see tetrachloroethane*
acids 2,3,7,15,16,17,21,29
acrylic 13
acrylic emulsions 8
aerosol sprays 1,6,7,19,20
airbrush 7,19
alcohols 4,6,28
aliphatic hydrocarbons, *see petroleum distillates*
alkalis 2,3,7,8,9,21,28
allergies 3,12,13,15,16,17,21
alum 7
amine catalysts 11
amines 3,14
ammonia 3,8,17
ammonium dichromate 16,18
amyl alcohol 6
anemia 3,4,5,7
aniline 3,4
anthrax 17
antimony compunds 4,8,9
antimony trichloride 19
aplastic anemia 1
aromatic hydrocarbons 6
arsenic compounds 3,4,6,8
asbestos 2,9,10,15,16,21,22
asphaltum 15
asthma 3,10,12,14,15,20

B

barium 6
barium carbonate 9
barrier creams 29
benzene, *see benzol*
benzidine type dyes 6,18
benzine 1,7,15,18
benzol 1,2,3,4,5,6,15,22
bichromates 3
birth defects 4
bladder cancer 6,18
bleaches 2,17,19
blood 4,13
brazing 12
breast-feeding 5
bronchitis, chronic 3,17,18
brown lung 17
byssinosis 17

C

cadmium 4,5,6,8,9,12,15,19
calcium hydroxide 8
calcium oxide 8
cancer, bladder 6,18
cancer, liver 4,6,7,14
cancer, lung 2,9,11,12,16
cancer, sinus 10
cancer, skin 3,15,16
carbon arcs 16,17,23,29
carbon disulfide 4,5
carbon black 15
carbon monoxide 4,5,6,7,9,11
carbon tetrachloride 6,16,18,22
casting metal 10,11
caustic soda, *see sodium hydroxide*
cellosolve 4,7
central nervous system 4
ceramics 9
children 5,20
chlorinated hydrocarbons 3,4,5,6,7,11,17,19,28
chlorine 16,20
chloroform 6
chrome alum 16,17
chrome yellow, *see lead chromate*
chrome yellow 15,19
chromic acid 7,17
chromium compounds 8,9,12
chronic disease 1
clays 9,10,21
clothing, protective 29
coal tar derivatives 3
cold water dyes 3,18
color developers 17
commercial art 19
conjunctivitis 11
copper fumes 12
copper sulfate 17,19
cotton dust 17
cyanoacrylate 10

D

degreasing 11
dermatitis 3,6,16,17,18,19,28
dichloromethane, *see methylene chloride*
dioxane 4
disposal 27
driers, metallic 8
dust, metal 11,12,27
dust, wood 3,27
Dutch mordant 15
dyes 3,4,6,17,18,19,21

E

ear muffs 30
ear plugs 30
EDTA 20
emphysema 3,11,16,17,18
epoxy hardeners 3,13
epoxy resins 3,10,13,14
esters 7
etching 15
ethanol 6,8,20

ether 4,7,15
ethyl alcohol, *see ethanol*
ethylene dichloride 6,13,20
ethylene glycol monoethyl ether, *see cellosolve*
ethylene glycol monomethyl ether,
   see methyl cellosolve
exhaust hoods 23
explosions 15,20,25
eye protection 29
eyes, light damage 11,29

F

face protection 29
fans, exhaust 23,25
feldspar 9
ferric ammonium citrate 17
fertility 4,5
fiberglass 3,15
fibers 17
fire extinguishers 26
fixer, photographic 17
flammability 20,25
flashpoints 25,26
flax dust 17
flint 9
fluorocarbons 14,20
fluxes, fluoride 12,18
formaldehyde 3,10,11,17,21
formic acid 17
fountain solutions 16
French chalk 16
freons, *see fluorocarbons*
frits 9,21
fumes, welding 2,3,12

G

gasoline 7
glazes, ceramic 9,21
gloves 28
goggles 29
granite 10
grinders consumption 10
gum arabic 20

H

hand cleansers 29
hearing 30
heart 6,20
heat cataracts 11
heat stress 11
hemp dust 17
hepatitis 4
hexamethylenetetramine 11
hexane 4,7,19
housekeeping 26
hydrochloric acid 7,15,17
hydrofluoric acid 7,18,19
hydrogen chloride 14
hydrogen cyanide 4,17,20
hydrogen peroxide 16
hydroquinone 16
hypo 17

I

infrared light 11,29
inks 19
intaglio 15
iodine 20
iron chromate 9
isocyanates 3,14

J

jaundice 4

K

kaolin 9
kerosene 7,21
ketones 3,4,7,28
kidneys 5,6,20
kilns 9

L

labelling 1,21,26
lacquer thinners 6,9,21,26,28
lamp black 3,8,16
lead 2,3,4,5,6,8,9,10,11,12,15,18,21
lead chromate 8,9,15,19
leukemia 1,4,6,10
lithography 16
liver 6
liver cancer 4,6,7,14
liver cirrhosis 4
liver of sulfur 17
lungs 3
lung cancer 2,9,11,12,16

M

manganese 5,8,9,12,19
markers, felt 19,21
menstrual disorders 4
mercuric chloride 17
mercury compounds 4,8,17
mesothelioma 10,16
metal dusts, *see dusts, metal*
metal fumes 10,12
metal fume fever 11
metals, heavy 4,8
methanol 2,6,8,10,21
methyl alcohol, *see methanol*
methyl butyl ketone 4,7
methyl cellosolve 7
methyl cellosolve acetate 7,16
methyl chloroform 6,13,20
methyl ethyl ketone 7,40
methyl methacrylate 13
methylene chloride 5,6,10,13,14,28
metol 16
mineral spirits 7,8
mordants 17,18
mutagens 5

N

naphtha 4,7
narcosis 6,19
nasal cancer 10
nervous system 4
nickel carbonyl 12

nickel compounds 3,7,9,12
nitric acid 3,7,8,15,16,20
nitrogen oxides 3,11,15,16,17
noise, protection against 10,29

O

oxalic acid 17,18
ozone 3,11,16,17

P

paint 8,19
paint strippers 1,6,7,10,21,28
paint thinner 6,7,21
paraffins 3
Parkinson's disease 12
perchloric acid 7
perchloroethylene 6
peripheral neuritis 4,7,19
peroxides 2,13
personal hygiene 26
petroleum distillates 3,7,19,28
petroleum ether 7
phenol 2,4,7
phosgene 7,11,12
phosphoric acid 16
phototechniques 16
photographic developers 4,16
photography 16,21
photoprinting 18
photoresists 16
physical hazards 27
pigments 8,19
plaster of paris 10
plastics 12
plastics, catalysts 13,14
platinum 17
pneumatic tools 10
pneumonia 3,10,14
polyester 13,28
polymer fume fever 14
polystyrene 14
polyurethane 3,4,11,14
polyvinyl acetate 14
polyvinyl alcohol 14
polyvinyl chloride 14
potassium carbonate 8
potassium dichromate 16,17,21
potassium ferricyanide 17,18
potassium hydroxide 8
potassium iodate 20
potassium permanganate 20
potters rot 9
pregnancy 4,5
primary irritants 3
print-making 15
protective equipment, sources of, Appendix
pulmonary edema 3,6,7,8,12,14,15,18,19
pulmonary fibrosis 3

Q

quartz 10
quicklime 8

R

relief printing 15
reproductive system 4,5
respirators 27
respirator, care of 28
respirator, choosing 27,28
respirator, sources of, Appendix
retouching 20
risk factor 2,21
rosin 15,16
rubber cement 4,19,21
rubber cement thinner 4,7,14,19

S

safety equipment 27
sandstone 10
selenium 17,19
sensitizers, dichromate 16
serpentine 10
shellac 6,8
shellac thinner 6
silica 3,9,10,11,15
silicone rubber 14
silicosis 9,10,11
silk screening 6,15
silver nitrate 16,18,19
silver soldering 12
sinus cancer 10
skin 2,3,28
skin cancer 3,15,16
skin creams 29
skin products, sources of, Appendix
skin protection 28
smoking 2,3,5,6,7,14,26
soapstone 10
sodium bisulfite 20
sodium carbonate 8,16
sodium cyanide 20
sodium dichromate 18
sodium dithionite, see sodium hydrosulfite
sodium hydrosulfite 18,20
sodium hydroxide 8,16,18
sodium metasilicate 8
sodium silicate 8
sodium sulfate 18
sodium sulfite 16,17
sodium thiosulphate 17
soldering 11,12,18,21
solvents 3,4,5,6,15,19,21,22,25,27,28
solvents, aromatic 3,6,15,29
solvents, flammability 20,25,26
solvents, flash points 25,26
solvents, printmaking 15
spills 26,27
spray booth 23
sprays 7,19,21,23
stained glass 18,21
stainless steel welding 12
stannous chloride 20
stone 9,10
stonemasons disease 10
stop bath 16,17
storage 26

styrene 4,13,14,26
styrofoam 11,14
sulfur dioxide 9,17,18,20
sulfuric acid 7,18,20

T

talc 16,17
teratogens 5
tetrachloroethane 6
textiles 17
thermoplastics 12
thermosetting plastics 12
thiourea 20
toluene, see toluol
toluol 2,3,4,5,6,7,8,9,10,15,16,19,28
toxicity 2
1,1,1-trichloroethane, see methyl chloroform
trichloroethylene 5,6
turpentine 3,7,8,9,21,26

U

ultraviolet light 11,16,18,29
uranium 9,17

V

vanadium 9
varnishes 9
vehicles, pigment 8
ventilation, dilution 23,25
ventilation, local exhaust 23
vibration 10
vinyl chloride 5,7,14
vinyl toluene 13

W

wax fumes 18
weaving 17
welding 11,23,29
welding hood 23
woods 10
wood dust 3,10,21,27

X

xylene, see xylol
xylol 4,5,6,9,15,19,26,28

Z

zinc chloride 12,18
zinc chromate 8,9,15,19
zinc fumes 11,12,18
zinc yellow, see zinc chromate

About the FCA

The Foundation for the Community of Artists is a nonprofit, tax-exempt, artists' membership organization. Membership costs $10 annually and includes a subscription to *Art-Workers News*. The Foundation's activities include the following projects:

Art Workers News: An artist-run newspaper, published 10 times a year (circulation 5,000), concerned with housing, artists' rights, legislation, health hazards, grant opportunities, news of importance to working artists, and much more. The cost of a one year subscription is $8 for artists and $12 for institutions and libraries.

Art Work: A federally funded employment agency providing job development, counselling, and placement for artists.

Task Force on Discrimination Against Women & Minorities in Art: A CETA program to research discrimination in New York City and provide counselling to artists involved.

Health & Hospitalization Insurance: Group insurance programs for artists in New York State.

Books for The Arts: The Foundation's publications include the *Artists' Health Hazards Manual, Artists' Estate Planning Guide,* and the *AntiCatalog.* In addition, the Foundation distributes books of importance to artists such as *Legal Guide for the Visual Artist, Money Business: Grants and Awards to Creative Artists, Pricing and Ethical Guidelines, Artists' Associations in the USA,* and *The Visual Artist's Guide to the New Copyright Law.* All publications are available at a discount to members.

Artists' Housing: The Foundation maintains an advocacy position on all aspects of artists' housing and is preparing a Housing Manual for publication.

Artists' Rights and Legislation: The Foundation provides information to artists and legislators about legislation and regulations concerning tax reform, resale, copyright, estate tax provisions, and the "hobby loss" problem. The Foundation is working with others to bring about change in the grant priority system of the New York State Council on the Arts and the National Endowment for the Arts.

Artists' Apprenticeship Program: The Foundation is developing an apprenticeship program through CETA designed to train young artists by assisting working artists in their studios.

What's Ahead: The Foundation is hoping to initiate programs for legal insurance, a credit union and a "Housing Hot Line" to deal with artists' housing problems.

FOUNDATION FOR THE COMMUNITY OF ARTISTS: MEMBERSHIP AND SUBSCRIPTION ORDER
280 Broadway, Suite 412·New York, NY 10007·212/227-3770

DATE / /

NAME (Please type or print clearly)

STREET ADDRESS

CITY   STATE   ZIPCODE

Write checks payable to: Foundation for the Community of Artists   ☐ Check enclosed

Foreign subscribers: Add $1.00 to rates for Canada & Mexico; add $2.00 for all other countries.

INDIVIDUALS
☐ $15.00 Membership & Subscription
☐ $8.00 Subscription Only
☐ Renewal

INSTITUTIONS & LIBRARIES
☐ $12.00 Subscription or Renewal

DONATION $ _____

INDIVIDUALS PLEASE INDICATE CATEGORY
☐ Artist
☐ Commercial Artist
☐ Artist/Teacher
☐ Filmmaker or Video Artist
☐ Photographer
☐ Museum or Council Worker
☐ Art Historian

☐ Other _____

37

Publications

FCA Books for The Arts

An Anti-Catalog *Rudolph Baranik, Elaine Bendock, Sarina Bromberg, Sarah Charlesworth, Susanne Cohn, Carol Duncan, Shawn Gargagliano, Eunice Golden, Janet Koenig, Joseph Kosuth, Anthony McCall, Paul Pechter, Aaron Roseman, Larry Rosing, Ann-Marie Rousseau, Alan Wallach, Walter Weissman. The Catalog Committee, NY, NY, 1977; 80 pps.* The Catalog Committee is a collective of artists and art historians that have been associated with Artists Meeting for Cultural Change. An Anti-Catalog began as a part of a protest against an exhibition of American art belonging to John D. Rockefeller III, which was held at the Whitney Museum of Art in the Fall of 1976. The issues it addresses, however, transcend this particular exhibition, and the critical outlook it communicates raises questions about the practice of museums and established art history in general. Written and pictorial essays explore the way art is mystified, how art exhibitions influence our view of history, and how collectors such as JDRIII benefit from cultural philanthropy. Specific essays also look at women, blacks, native American art, landscape painting and portraiture. ISBN 0-933032-02-1 **$5.00; $4.00 FCA members.** Stock #NF201

Artists' Associations in the USA *Helen Shlien. The Boston Visual Artists Association, Boston, 1977; 310 pps.* This paperback book lists over 1600 visual artists organizations and is descriptive of more than 400 groups including the number and type of membership as well as their functions. A bibliography contains source information on legal and health problems with an appendix on artists' rights. **$4.00; $3.50 FCA members.** Stock #D100

Artists Estate Planning Guide *James R. Cohen. FCA, NY, NY, 1978; 16 pps.* An up-to-date pamphlet on the crucial problems that face artists when planning their estates. With an introduction and extensive footnotes, this pamphlet is an indispensable guide for accountants, attorneys and advisors to artists. ISBN 0-933032-01-3 **$1.95; $1.50 FCA members.** Stock #M013

Artists Health Hazards Manual *Michael McCann, PhD. FCA, NY, NY; 1978; 48 pps.* The revised and expanded edition of the best selling manual detailing the health risks that artists dare not be ignorant of. Includes introduction, bibliography and index. ISBN 0-933032-00-5 **$3.50; $2.75 FCA members.** Stock #M005

Money Business: Grants and Awards for Creative Artists *The Artists Foundation, Boston, 1978; 108 pps.* The unique guide to 300 organizations around the country that offer grants and awards to individual professional artists, including listings for painters, printmakers, sculptors, photographers, playwrights, poets, writers, composers, and to a limited extent, filmmakers, video artists and choreographers. Special sections cover artists' retreats as well as programs that directly assist individual artists. **$7.00; $5.75 FCA members.** Stock #D303

ArtWorkers News *The Foundation for the Community of Artists, NY, NY.* An artist-run newspaper, published 10 times a year (circulation 5,000), concerned with housing, artists' rights, legislation, health and safety hazards, grant opportunities, CETA programs and news of importance to working artists. **$8.00 Individual subscription (1 yr.);** *$12.00 Institutions and libraries (1 yr.).* Stock #AWN

The Writer's Legal Guide *Tad Crawford. Hawthorn Books NY, NY, 1978; 273 pps.* Covers all the legal areas with which writers in all fields—fiction, non-fiction, poetry, drama, television, and film—must be familiar. Included are the new copyright law, defamation, invasion of privacy, publishing and agency contracts, income taxation, censorship, vanity presses, and public support for writers. Model contracts illustrate key points. The appendices include a list of lawyers groups volunteering to aid needy writers. ISBN 0-80-158937-1 **$10.95;** *$9.50 FCA members.* Stock #M371

Legal Guide for the Visual Artist *Tad Crawford. Hawthorn Books, NY, NY, 1977;*

259 pps. The definitive guide on legal problems of the artist. Areas covered include copyright, general rights of the artist, sales (by artist, gallery, agent), reproduction rights, publishing and dealer contracts, video works, loft leases, income taxation, the artist as collector, donations to museums, and public support for artists. Model contracts are included as well as lists of artists' groups, organizations for the arts, state arts agencies, and lawyers groups to assist artists. ISBN 0-8015-4471-8 **$9.95;** *$8.95 FCA members.* Stock #M718

The Visual Artists Guide to the New Copyright Law *Tad Crawford. Graphic Artists Guild, NY, NY, 1978; 64 pps.* An essential guide for all artists to the provisions of the new copyright law that became effective on January 1, 1978. Readable, practical and thorough. It covers what is copyrightable, who can benefit from copyright, what the rights of a copyright owner are, the proper forms of copyright

notice, the advantages of registration and what forms to use, how to avoid having to deposit original artwork with the Copyright Office, the work-for-hire pitfall, special rules for selling to magazines, and the doctrine of fair use. This 64 page pamphlet contains copies of the Copyright Office's application forms, appendices on educational fair use and the definition of the "best edition" of a work and an index. ISBN 0-932102-00-X **$5.50;** *$3.50 FCA members.* Stock #M00-X

Pricing and Ethical Guidelines Graphic Artists Guild, NY, NY, 1978; 50 pps. This is the only comprehensive guide to fair prices and business practices in every phase of the graphic arts. As a set of standards on codes and ethics in the graphic arts, officially practiced and promoted in the industry, this guide by the Graphic Artists Guild is a valuable business tool in the profession. **$8.00;** *$7.25 FCA members.* Stock #M202

FOUNDATION FOR THE COMMUNITY OF ARTISTS·280 BROADWAY, SUITE 412·NY, NY 10007

Please send the following books/publications to:

DATE / /

NAME

STREET ADDRESS

CITY   STATE   ZIPCODE

Write checks payable to: Foundation for the Community of Artists   ☐ Check enclosed

Add $.50 on the first title and $.20 for each additional title for postage and handling. Orders from libraries and institutions, etc. will be billed for actual postage costs. Foreign airmail: $1.00 per title for Canada and Mexico; $2.00 for all other countries.

QUAN	TITLE	STOCK #	PRICE
		TOTAL $	